PRIMARY MATHEMATICS

WORKBOOK 1B

Common Core Edition

SINGAPORE MATH® PROGRAM

Marshall Cavendish Education

US Distributor

SM Singapore Math Inc.®

Original edition published under the title Primary Mathematics Workbook 1B
© 1981 Curriculum Planning & Development Division, Ministry of Education, Singapore
Published by Times Media Private Limited

This edition © 2014 Marshall Cavendish Education Pte Ltd
(Formerly known as Marshall Cavendish International (Singapore) Private Limited)

Published by Marshall Cavendish Education
Times Centre, 1 New Industrial Road, Singapore 536196
Customer Service Hotline: (65) 6213 9444
US Office Tel: (1-914) 332 8888 | Fax: (1-914) 332 8882
E-mail: tmesales@mceducation.com
Website: www.mceducation.com

Distributed by
Singapore Math Inc.®
19535 SW 129th Avenue
Tualatin, OR 97062
Tel: (503) 557 8100
Website: www.singaporemath.com

First published 2014

Singapore Math® is a trademark of Singapore Math Inc.® and
Marshall Cavendish Education Pte Ltd.

Primary Mathematics (Common Core Edition) Workbook 1B
ISBN 978-981-01-9842-8

Printed in Singapore

Primary Mathematics (Common Core Edition) is adapted from Primary Mathematics Workbook 1B (3rd Edition), originally
developed by the Ministry of Education, Singapore. This edition contains new content developed by Marshall Cavendish
Education Pte Ltd, which is not attributable to the Ministry of Education, Singapore.

We would like to acknowledge the contributions by:

The Project Team from the Ministry of Education, Singapore, that developed the original Singapore edition
Project Director: Dr Kho Tek Hong
Team Members: Hector Chee Kum Hoong, Liang Hin Hoon, Lim Eng Tann, Ng Siew Lee, Rosalind Lim Hui Cheng, Ng Hwee Wan

Primary Mathematics (Common Core Edition)
Richard Askey, Emeritus Professor of Mathematics from University of Wisconsin, Madison
Jennifer Kempe, Curriculum Advisor from Singapore Math Inc.®

CONTENTS

EXERCISE 1

1. Circle groups of 10. Then count and write the number.

24

2. Fill in the blanks.

38 is 30 and 8.

30 + 8 = _____

15 is 10 and _____.

10 + 5 = _____

24 is 20 and _____.

20 + 4 = _____

32 is 30 and _____.

30 + 2 = _____

3. Fill in the blanks.

19 and 1 make 20.

19 + 1 = _____

20 and 6 make _____.

20 + 6 = _____

30 and 3 make _____.

30 + 3 = _____

39 and 1 make _____.

39 + 1 = _____

EXERCISE 2

1. Match.

2. Write the numbers.

36
thirty-six

twenty-five

thirty-nine

thirty-two

thirty

thirty-four

twenty-eight

twenty-seven

twenty-four

thirty-three

EXERCISE 3

1. Fill in the missing numbers.

(a)

1 more than 20 is _____.

(b)

3 more than 30 is _____.

(c)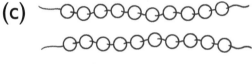

7 more than 20 is _____.

(d)

5 more than 30 is _____.

EXERCISE 4

1. Fill in the missing numbers.

(a)

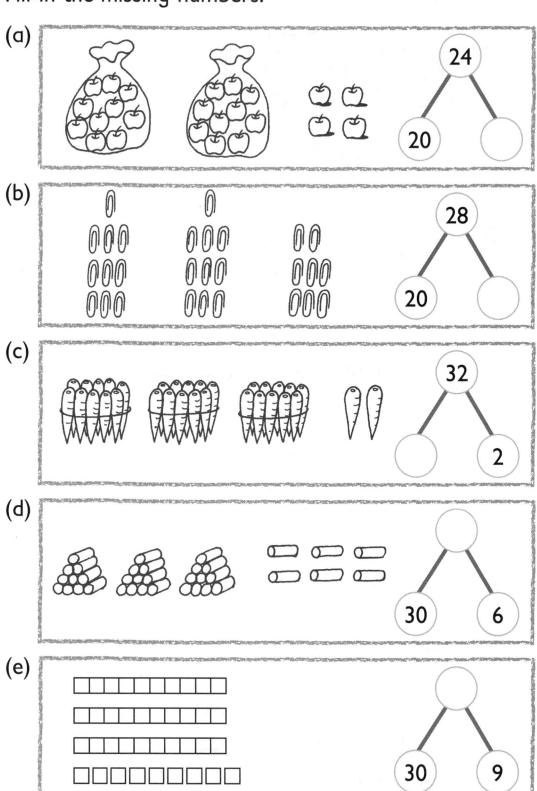

(b)

(c)

(d)

(e)

2. Fill in the missing numbers.

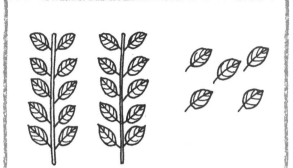

20 + 5 = ☐

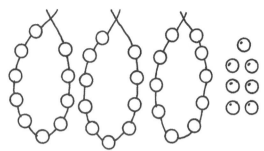

30 + 7 = ☐

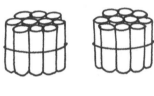

20 + ☐ = 26

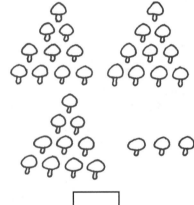

30 + ☐ = 33

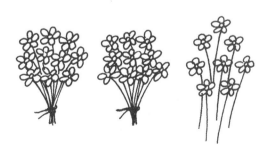

☐ + 8 = 28

☐ + 4 = 34

EXERCISE 5

1. Fill in the missing numbers.

(a)

11 12 ( ) ( ) 15 ( ) 17 ( ) 19

(b)

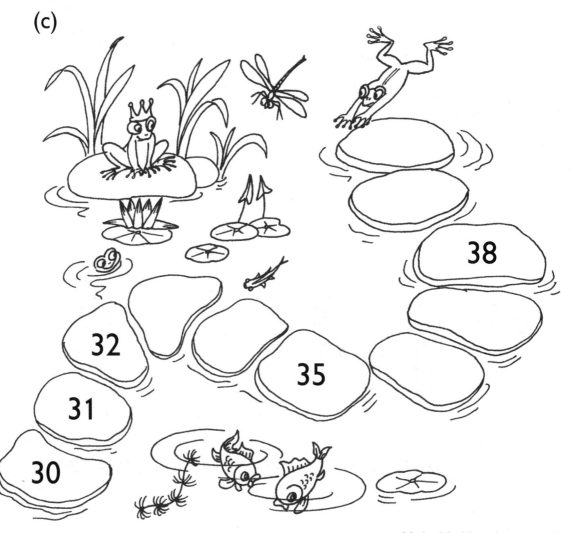

21			24		26	27			30

(c)

38

32

35

31

30

2.

1	2	3	4	5	6	7	8	9	10
11	12	13	14	15	16	17	18	19	20
21	22	23	24	25	26	27	28	29	30
31	32	33	34	35	36	37	38	39	40

Fill in the blanks.

Use the chart above to help you.

(a) 1 more than 15 is _____.

(b) 1 more than 26 is _____.

(c) 1 more than 30 is _____.

(d) 1 less than 18 is _____.

(e) 1 less than 33 is _____.

(f) 1 less than 40 is _____.

(g) 2 more than 17 is _____.

(h) 2 more than 29 is _____.

(i) 2 less than 28 is _____.

(j) 2 less than 37 is _____.

EXERCISE 6

1. Write how many tens and ones.

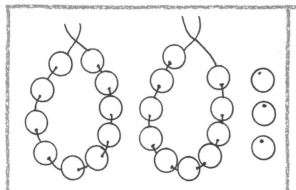

23 = ___ tens ___ ones

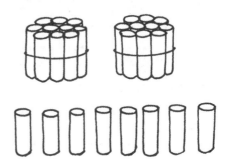

28 = ___ tens ___ ones

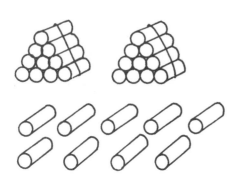

29 = ___ tens ___ ones

26 = ___ tens ___ ones

38 = ___ tens ___ ones

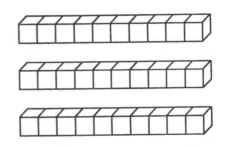

30 = ___ tens ___ ones

2. Write how many tens and ones.
   Then write the number.

(a)

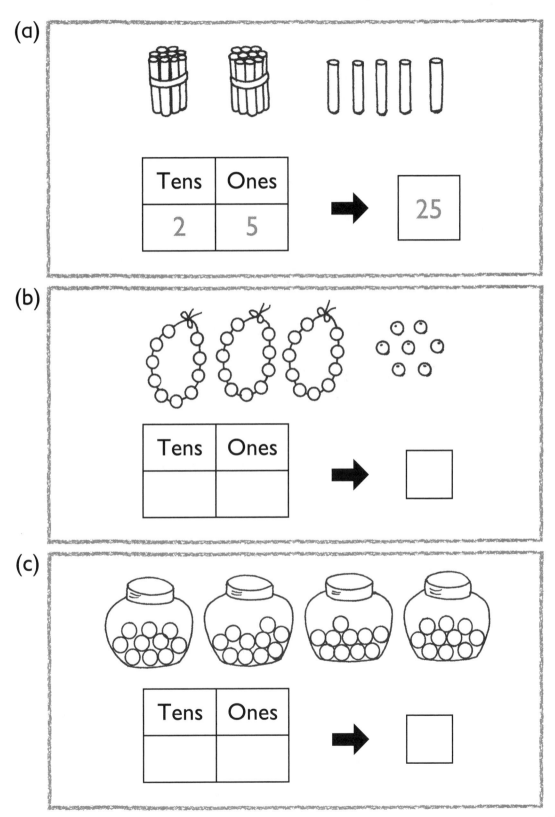

Tens	Ones
2	5

➡ 25

(b)

Tens	Ones

➡ ☐

(c)

Tens	Ones

➡ ☐

EXERCISE 7

1. Fill in the blanks.

(a)

1 more than 18 is _____.

(b)

10 more than 23 is _____.

(c)

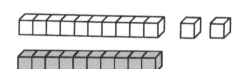

10 more than 12 is _____.

(d)

1 more than 39 is _____.

2. Fill in the blanks.

(a)

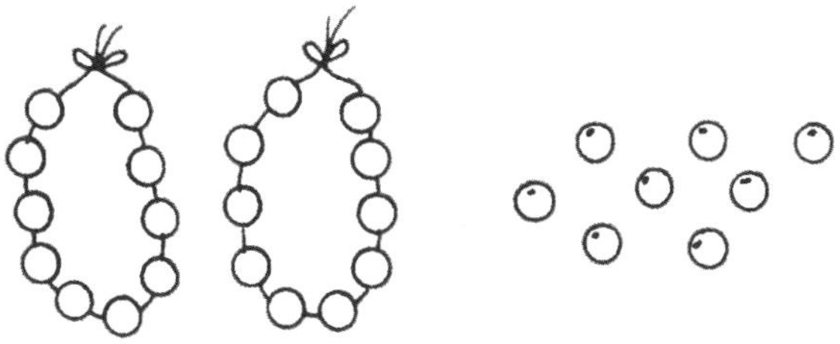

1 less than 28 is _____.

(b)

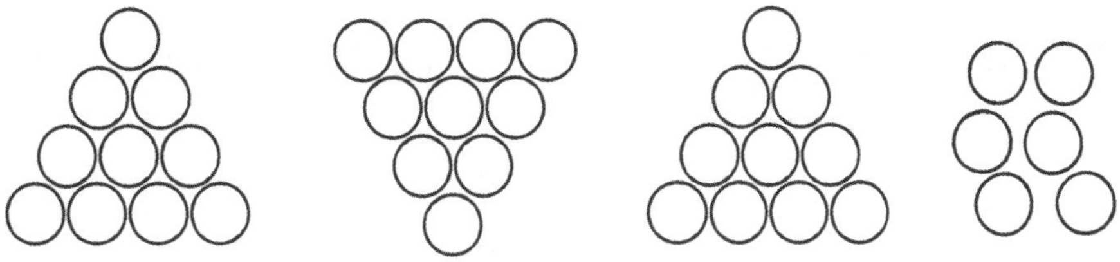

10 less than 36 is _____.

(c)

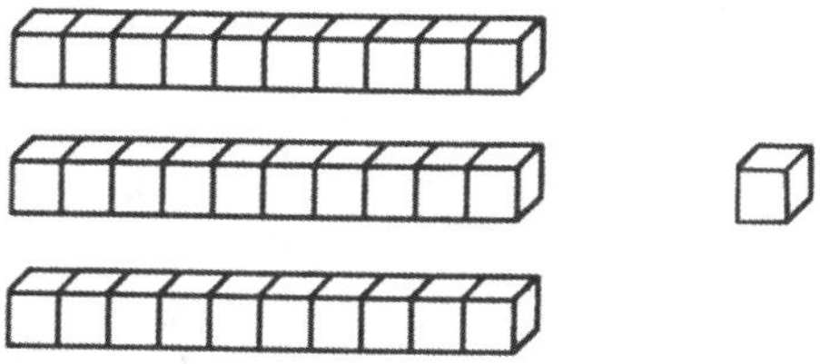

1 less than 31 is _____.

(d)

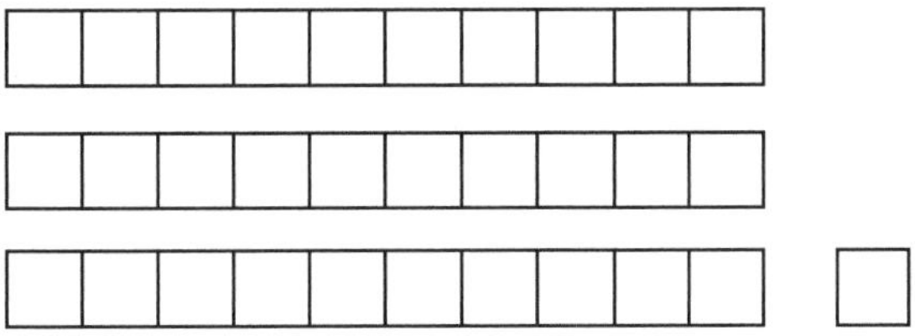

10 less than 31 is _____.

3. Fill in the blanks.

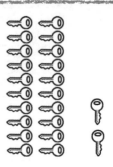

1 more than 25 is _____.

10 more than 25 is _____.

1 less than 22 is _____.

10 less than 22 is _____.

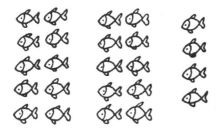

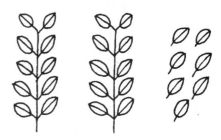

1 more than 24 is _____.

10 more than 24 is _____.

1 more than 27 is _____.

10 more than 27 is _____.

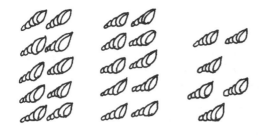

1 less than 26 is _____.

10 less than 26 is _____.

1 less than 29 is _____.

10 less than 29 is _____.

EXERCISE 8

1. Use the numbers in the bag to fill in the blanks.

    (a)

    38   25   40   21

    25 is greater than _____.

    38 is smaller than _____.

    The greatest number is _____.

    The smallest number is _____.

    (b)

    35   17   29   39

    29 is greater than _____.

    35 is smaller than _____.

    The greatest number is _____.

    The smallest number is _____.

EXERCISE 9

1. Add.

(a)

 4 + 2 =

 14 + 2 =

 24 + 2 =

(b)

 2 + 5 =

 22 + 5 =

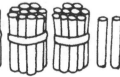 32 + 5 =

2. Subtract.

(a)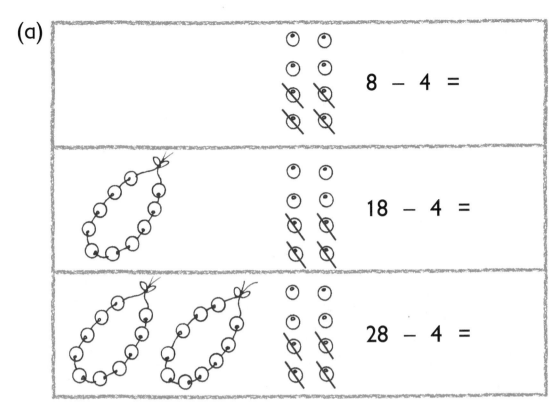

8 – 4 =

18 – 4 =

28 – 4 =

(b)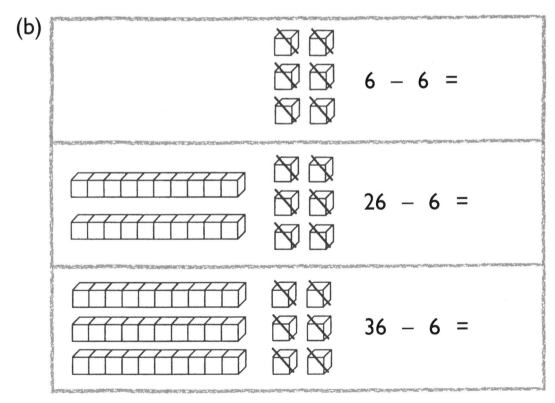

6 – 6 =

26 – 6 =

36 – 6 =

EXERCISE 10

1. Add.

(a)

$15 + 3 =$

(b)

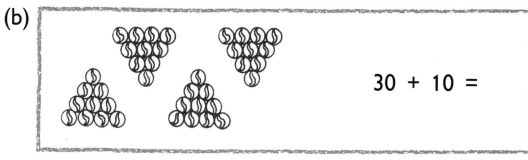

$30 + 10 =$

(c)

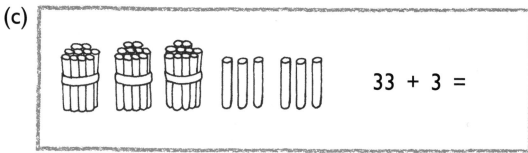

$33 + 3 =$

(d)

$12 + 10 =$

(e)

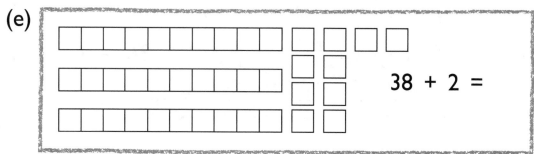

$38 + 2 =$

2. Subtract.

(a)
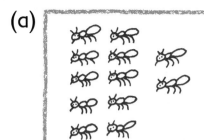
12 – 2 =

(b)

25 – 10 =

(c)
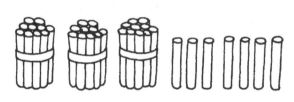
37 – 3 =

(d)
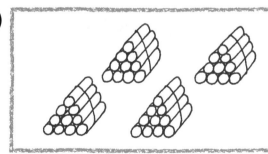
40 – 10 =

(e)
△△△△△△△△△   △ △
△△△△△△△△△   △ △   36 – 6 =
△△△△△△△△△   △ △

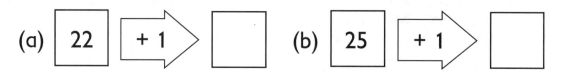

EXERCISE 11

1. Write the answers.

(a) | 22 | + 1 > ☐   (b) | 25 | + 1 > ☐

(c) | 28 | + 2 > ☐   (d) | 30 | + 2 > ☐

(e) | 34 | + 3 > ☐   (f) | 35 | + 3 > ☐

(g) | 33 | + 1 > ☐   (h) | 39 | + 1 > ☐

2. Write the answers.

(a) | 23 | − 1 > ☐   (b) | 26 | − 1 > ☐

(c) | 27 | − 2 > ☐   (d) | 30 | − 2 > ☐

(e) | 34 | − 3 > ☐   (f) | 39 | − 3 > ☐

(g) | 38 | − 1 > ☐   (h) | 40 | − 2 > ☐

3. Write the answers.

(a) (20) [+ 1] ⟹ ◯   (b) (30) [+ 1] ⟹ ◯

(c) (20) [− 1] ⟹ ◯   (d) (30) [− 1] ⟹ ◯

(e) (33) [+ 2] ⟹ ◯   (f) (34) [+ 0] ⟹ ◯

(g) (35) [− 2] ⟹ ◯   (h) (32) [− 2] ⟹ ◯

(i) (36) [+ 3] ⟹ ◯   (j) (37) [+ 3] ⟹ ◯

(k) (39) [− 3] ⟹ ◯   (l) (40) [− 3] ⟹ ◯

4. Follow the arrows and fill in the missing numbers.

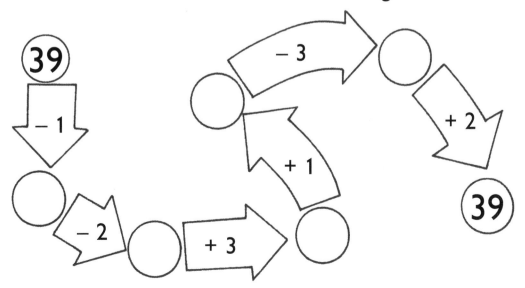

EXERCISE 12

1. Add.

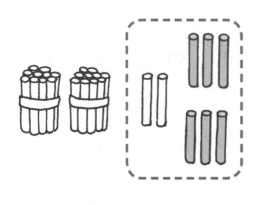

22 + 6 =

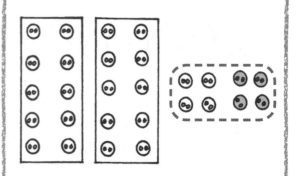

24 + 4 =

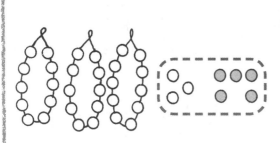

33 + 5 =

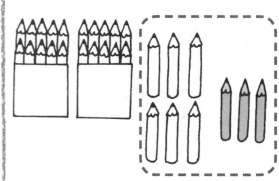

26 + 3 =

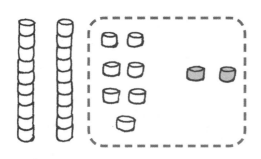

27 + 2 =

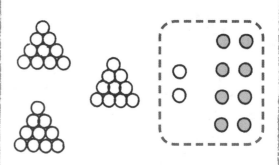

32 + 8 =

Unit 11: Numbers to 40

2. Add.

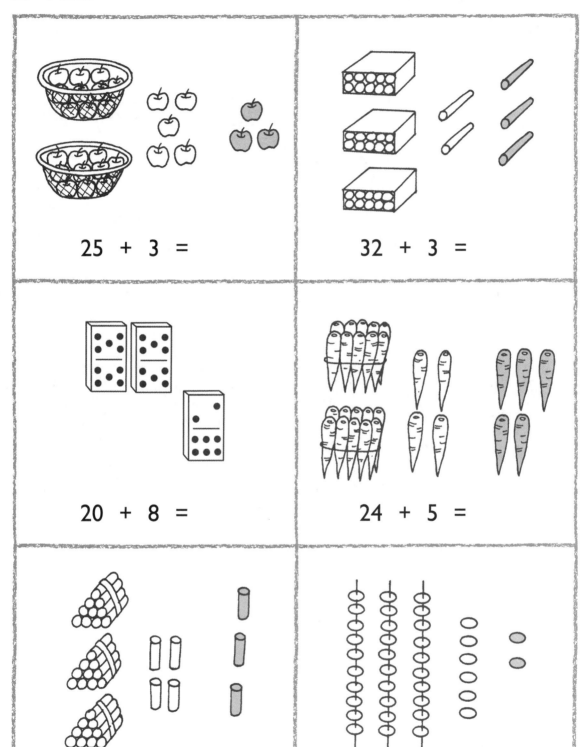

25 + 3 =

32 + 3 =

20 + 8 =

24 + 5 =

34 + 3 =

36 + 2 =

EXERCISE 13

1. Add.

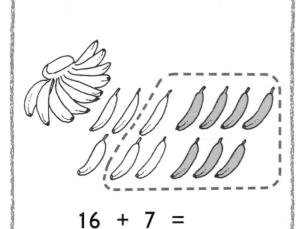

16 + 7 =

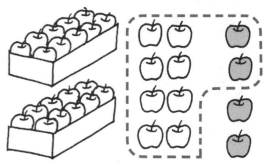

28 + 4 =

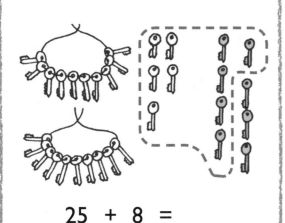

25 + 8 =

27 + 4 =

29 + 3 =

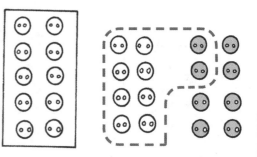

18 + 8 =

2. Add.

15 + 6 =

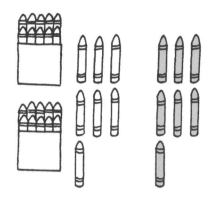

27 + 7 =

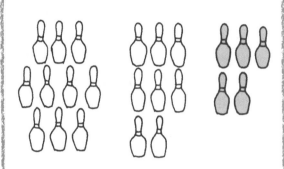

18 + 5 =

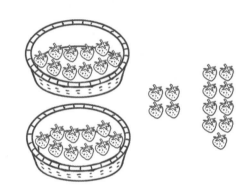

24 + 9 =

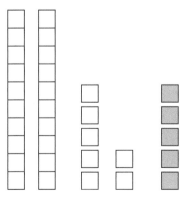

27 + 5 =

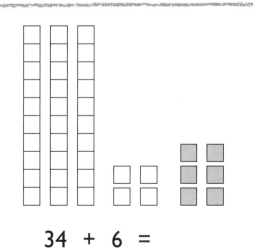

34 + 6 =

EXERCISE 14

1. Add.

7 + 8 → 15

8 + 8

9 + 7

6 + 9

5 + 9

9 + 9

7 + 6

4 + 8

9 + 8

6 + 5

8 + 7

7 + 7

6 + 8

8 + 9

7 + 5

8 + 5

EXERCISE 15

1. Add.

 4 + 3 = 7

 14 + 3 =

5 + 2 = 15 + 2 =	6 + 3 = 16 + 3 =
4 + 4 = 24 + 4 =	5 + 4 = 25 + 4 =
7 + 2 = 37 + 2 =	2 + 6 = 32 + 6 =

2. Add.

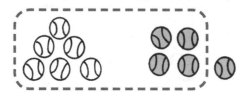

$6 + 5 = 11$

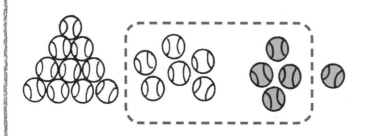

$16 + 5 =$

16 + 5
10   6

$7 + 3 =$ $17 + 3 =$	$8 + 3 =$ $18 + 3 =$
$6 + 6 =$ $26 + 6 =$	$7 + 5 =$ $27 + 5 =$
$9 + 5 =$ $29 + 5 =$	$4 + 6 =$ $34 + 6 =$

EXERCISE 16

1. Subtract.

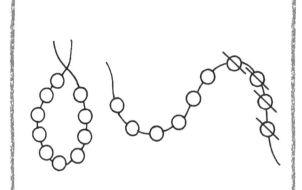

20 – 4 =

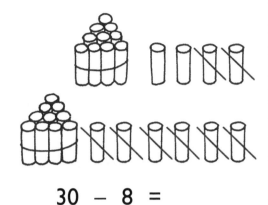

30 – 8 =

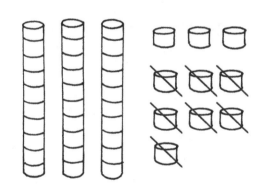

40 – 7 =

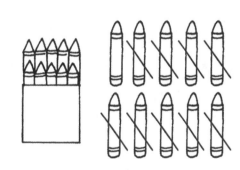

20 – 9 =

30 – 6 =

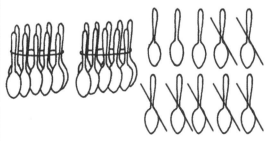

30 – 7 =

2. Subtract.

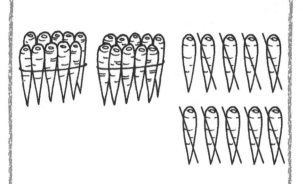

$$30 - 9 =$$

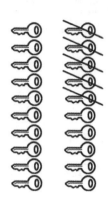

$$20 - 5 =$$

$$20 - 3 =$$

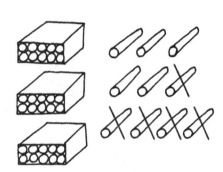

$$40 - 5 =$$

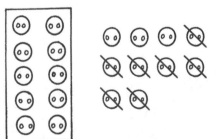

$$20 - 7 =$$

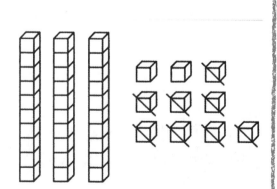

$$40 - 8 =$$

EXERCISE 17

1. Subtract.

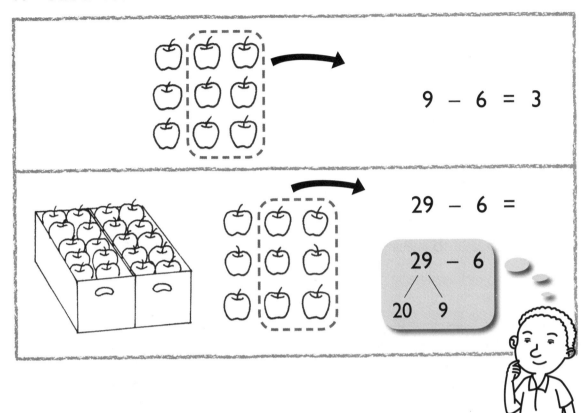

$$9 - 6 = 3$$

$$29 - 6 =$$

$$29 - 6$$
$$20 \quad 9$$

$8 - 5 =$ $38 - 5 =$	$6 - 4 =$ $26 - 4 =$
$5 - 3 =$ $25 - 3 =$	$9 - 7 =$ $39 - 7 =$
$7 - 3 =$ $37 - 3 =$	$8 - 6 =$ $28 - 6 =$

EXERCISE 18

1. Subtract.

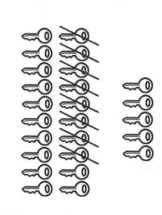

25 – 8 =

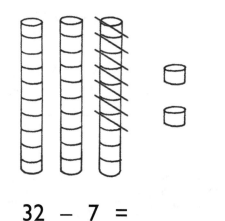

32 – 7 =

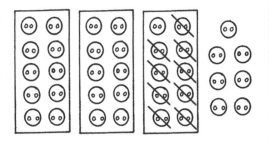

37 – 9 =

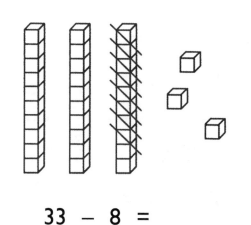

22 – 5 =

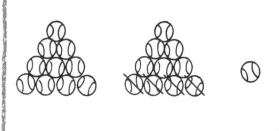

21 – 4 =

33 – 8 =

2. Subtract.

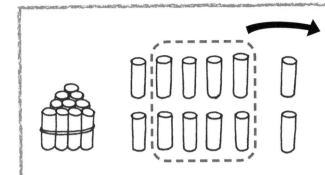

$$22 - 8 =$$

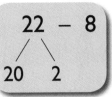

3. Subtract.

$40 - 7 =$	$38 - 4 =$
$22 - 10 =$	$26 - 9 =$
$34 - 8 =$	$25 - 6 =$
$30 - 7 =$	$32 - 5 =$
$25 - 3 =$	$31 - 7 =$

EXERCISE 19

1. Subtract and help the rabbit find its way to the carrot.

11 – 2 =

12 – 4 =

14 – 7 =

13 – 5 =

12 – 6 =

11 – 4 =

14 – 6 =

16 – 7 =

15 – 9 =

17 – 8 =

18 – 9 =

16 – 9 =

15 – 7 =

13 – 8 =

Unit 11: Numbers to 40

2. Subtract.

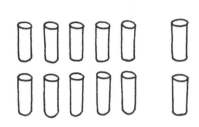 $12 - 8 = 4$

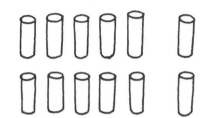

$22 - 8 =$

$14 - 7 =$ $34 - 7 =$	$15 - 8 =$ $25 - 8 =$
$17 - 9 =$ $27 - 9 =$	$11 - 6 =$ $21 - 6 =$
$13 - 5 =$ $33 - 5 =$	$18 - 9 =$ $38 - 9 =$

3. (a) Sam ate 24 carrots on Monday.
He ate 15 carrots on Tuesday.
How many carrots did he eat altogether?

$$\square \bigcirc \square = \square$$

He ate _____ carrots altogether.

(b) Mary gave away 16 stickers.
She gave away 19 stickers more.
How many stickers did she give away altogether?

$$\square \bigcirc \square = \square$$

She gave _____ stickers altogether.

(c) Tom made 38 cards.
He sent 17 cards.
How many more cards could he send?

$$\square \bigcirc \square = \square$$

He could send _____ more cards.

(d) Susan had to solve 40 questions.
She solved 18 questions.
How many questions were not solved?

$$\square \bigcirc \square = \square$$

_____ questions were not solved.

EXERCISE 20

1. Add.

(a)

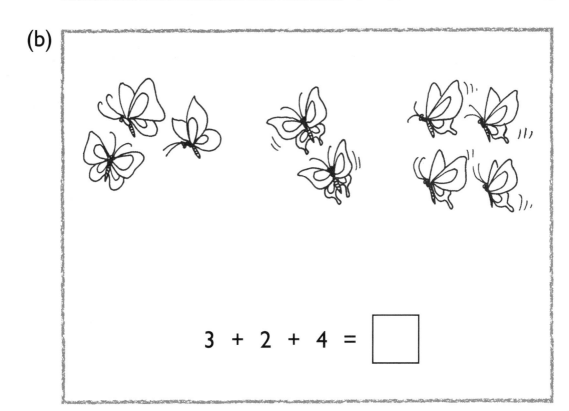

$$3 + 1 + 2 = \boxed{}$$

(b)

$$3 + 2 + 4 = \boxed{}$$

2. Add.

3 + 3 + 3 =

4 + 3 + 5 =

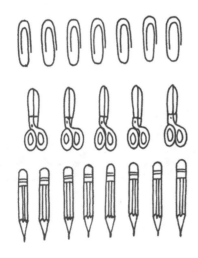

7 + 5 + 8 =

3 + 5 + 2 =

3. Add and write the answers in the circles.

(a)

1	6	5	→	(12)
8	4	0	→	◯
3	2	7	→	◯

↓   ↓   ↓

◯   ◯   ◯

(b)

2	7	6	→	◯
9	5	1	→	◯
4	3	8	→	◯

↓   ↓   ↓

◯   ◯   ◯

EXERCISE 21

1.

I bought 3 oranges.   I bought 5 oranges.   I bought 10 oranges.

Mr. Abbott   Mr. Walton   Mr. Garcia

How many oranges did they buy altogether?

     = ☐

They bought _____ oranges altogether.

2.

I have 5 balloons.   I have 1 balloon.   I have 6 balloons.

Ryan   Jose   Peter

How many balloons do they have altogether?

     = ☐

They have _____ balloons altogether.

3. Mrs. Ray buys 14 pears, 6 oranges, and 2 bananas.
   How many pieces of fruit are there altogether?

   $\boxed{} + \boxed{} + \boxed{} = \boxed{}$

   There are _____ pieces of fruits altogether.

4. Mr. Sam sold 6 pencils in the morning.
   He sold 3 pencils in the afternoon.
   He had 5 pencils left.
   How many pencils did Mr. Sam have at first?

   Mr. Sam had _____ pencils at first.

5. Eric has 8 toy trucks.
   He buys 7 more.
   His father gives him 2 toy trucks.
   How many toy trucks does he have now?

   He has _____ toy trucks now.

6. Lee had some cookies.
   He gave 3 cookies to his son.
   He also gave 10 cookies to Tom and 5 cookies to Lisa.
   He had no cookies left.
   How many cookies did Lee have at first?

   Lee had _____ cookies.

REVIEW 11

1. Write the numbers.
   Then match the numbers and words.

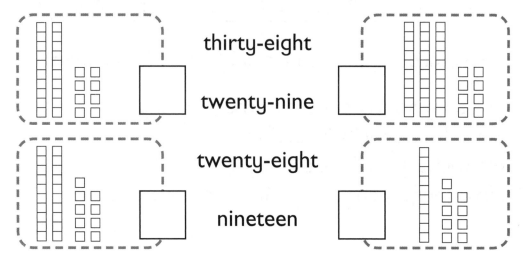

thirty-eight

twenty-nine

twenty-eight

nineteen

2. Fill in the missing numbers.

21	22			25				29	
		33				36			

3. Arrange the numbers in order.
   Begin with the smallest number.

———, ———, ———, ———, ————

smallest

4. Fill in the blanks.

   (a) 25 = 2 tens _____ ones

   (b) What number is 3 tens 1 one? _____

5. Fill in the blanks.

   (a) 10 more than 19 is _____.

   (b) 10 less than 28 is _____.

6. Complete the equations.

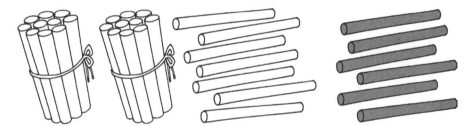

   (a) 27 + 6 = _____

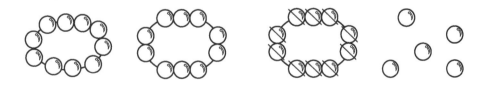

   (b) 35 − 8 = _____

7.

I have 6 stamps.

I have 4 stamps.

I have 5 stamps.

David

Tyrone

Ryan

How many stamps do they have altogether?

□ ◯ □ ◯ □ = □

They have _____ stamps altogether.

8.

I have 28 books.

I have 5 more books than Dakota.

Dakota

Lily

How many books does Lily have?

□ ◯ □ = □

Lily has _____ books.

9. Sarah buys 37 stickers.
   She gives 9 stickers away.
   How many stickers does she have left?

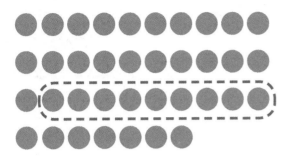

   She has _____ stickers left.

---

10. There are 19 children.
    6 children are jumping rope.
    How many children are not jumping rope?

    _____ children are not jumping rope.

11. There are 24 cupcakes altogether.
4 cupcakes are on the plate.
How many cupcakes are in the box?

_____ cupcakes are in the box.

---

12. There are 8 blue cars.
There are 4 yellow cars.
There are 6 red cars.
How many cars are there altogether?

There are _____ cars altogether.

EXERCISE 1

1. Write the answers.

$$2 + 2 + 2 =$$
3 twos $=$

$$3 + 3 + 3 + 3 =$$
4 threes $=$

$$6 + 6 =$$
2 sixes $=$

$$4 + 4 + 4 =$$
3 fours $=$

Unit 12: Multiplication

2. Complete the drawings. Then write the answers.

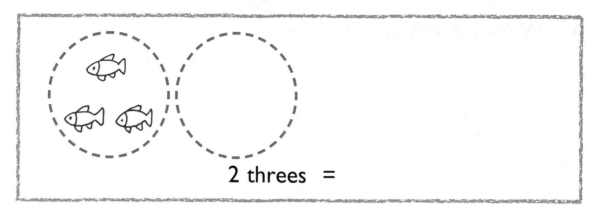

2 threes =

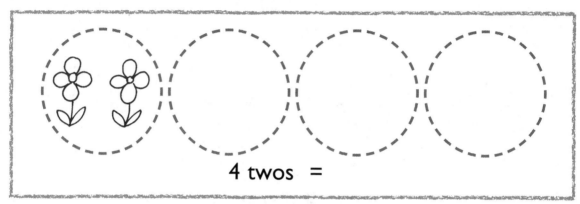

4 twos =

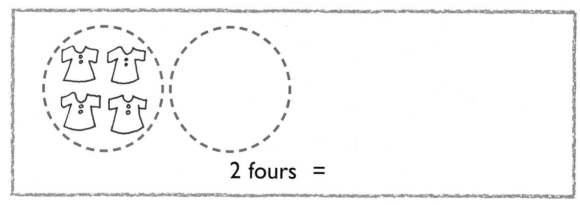

3 fives =

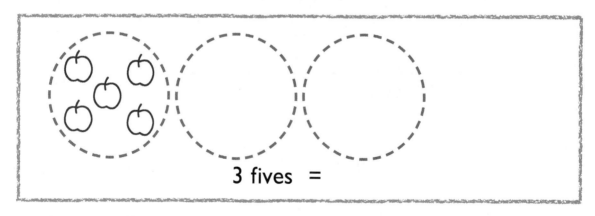

2 fours =

EXERCISE 2

1. Fill in the blanks.

(a)

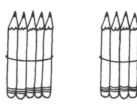

There are _____ pencils in each group.

There are _____ pencils altogether.

(b)

There are _____ cupcakes in each group.

There are _____ cupcakes altogether.

(c)

There are _____ carrots in each group.

There are _____ carrots altogether.

2. Complete the drawings. Then fill in the blanks.

(a)

There are 2 fish in each tank.

There are _____ fish altogether.

(b)

There are 3 apples in each bowl.

There are _____ apples altogether.

(c)
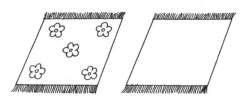

There are 4 buttons on each shirt.

There are _____ buttons altogether.

(d)

There are 5 flowers on each rug.

There are _____ flowers altogether.

Unit 12: Multiplication

EXERCISE 3

1. Fill in the blanks.

(a)

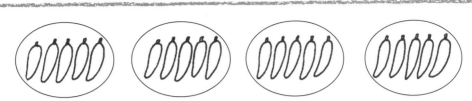

There are _____ groups of 5.

There are _____ peppers altogether.

(b)

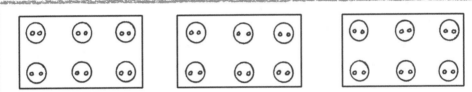

There are _____ groups of 6.

There are _____ buttons altogether.

(c)

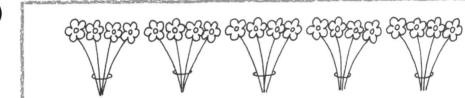

There are 5 groups of _____.

There are _____ flowers altogether.

(d)

There are 6 groups of _____.

There are _____ leaves altogether.

2. (a)

Draw 5 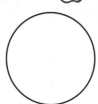 in each circle.

3 groups of 5 =

(b)

Draw 3 in each triangle.

4 groups of 3 =

(c)

Draw 4 in each square.

2 groups of 4 =

(d)

Draw 2 in each rectangle.

5 groups of 2 =

Unit 12: Multiplication

3. Fill in the blanks.

(a)

There are _____ apples in each row.
There are _____ apples in each column.
There are _____ apples altogether.

(b)

There are _____ rabbits in each row.
There are _____ rabbits in each column.
There are _____ rabbits altogether.

(c)

There are _____ cherries in each row.
There are _____ cherries in each column.
There are _____ cherries altogether.

Unit 12: Multiplication

EXERCISE 4

1. Match.

5 fours

3 groups of 8

Multiply 5 and 4.

Multiply 6 and 3.

4 tens

6 groups of 3

5×4

3×8

6×3

4×10

3 eights

5 groups of 4

Multiply 3 and 8.

Multiply 4 and 10.

6 threes

4 groups of 10

2. Tell a story for each picture.
   Then complete the multiplication equation.

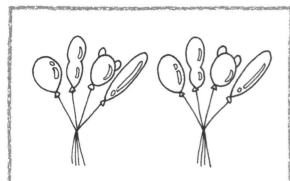

$\boxed{} \times \boxed{} = 8$ $\boxed{} \times \boxed{} = 20$

$\boxed{} \times \boxed{} = 9$ $\boxed{} \times \boxed{} = 10$

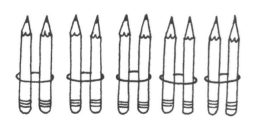

$\boxed{} \times \boxed{} = 10$ $\boxed{} \times \boxed{} = 12$

EXERCISE 5

1. (a)

Draw 🐟 to show 2 × 3 = 6.

(b)

Draw 🎈 to show 3 × 4 = 12.

(c)

Draw 🌼 to show 4 × 5 = 20.

(d)

Draw 🍎 to show 2 × 6 = 12.

EXERCISE 6

1. Match and write the answers.

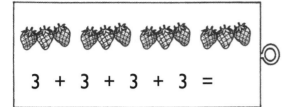

$3 + 3 + 3 + 3 =$

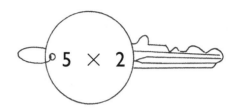

5×2

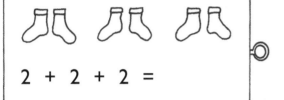

$2 + 2 + 2 =$

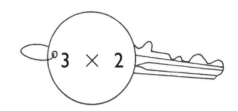

3×2

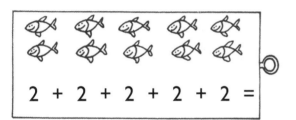

$2 + 2 + 2 + 2 + 2 =$

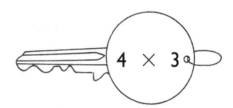

4×3

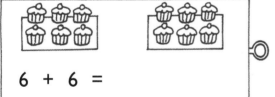

$6 + 6 =$

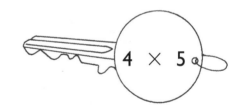

4×5

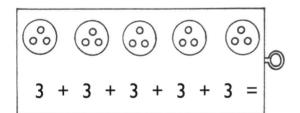

$3 + 3 + 3 + 3 + 3 =$

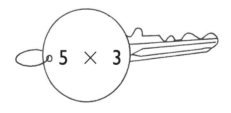

5×3

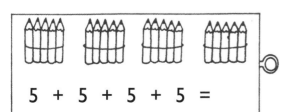

$5 + 5 + 5 + 5 =$

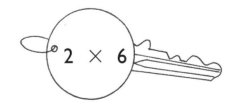

2×6

2. Write the answers.

(a)

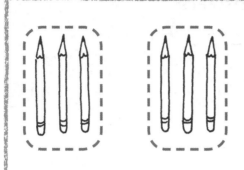

$2 \times 3 =$

(b)

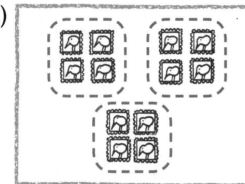

$3 \times 4 =$

(c)

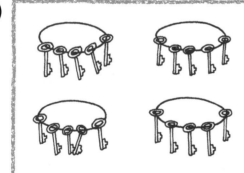

$4 \times 5 =$

(d)

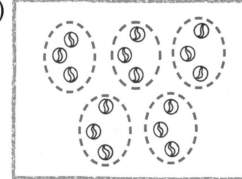

$5 \times 3 =$

Unit 12: Multiplication

3. Multiply.

(a)

$6 \times 2 =$

(b)
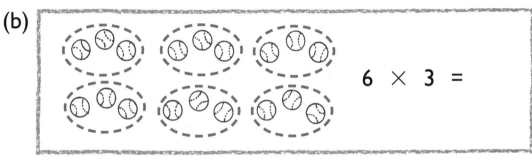
$6 \times 3 =$

(c)

$3 \times 4 =$

(d)
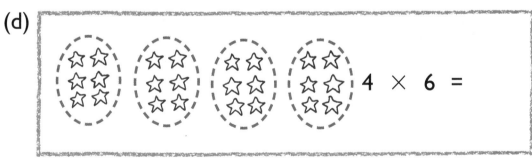
$4 \times 6 =$

(e)
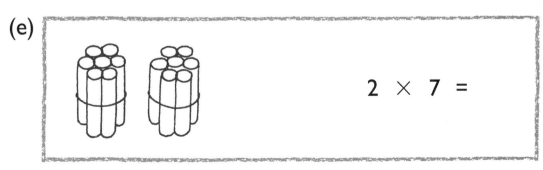
$2 \times 7 =$

EXERCISE 7

1.

How many apples are there altogether?

□ ○ □ = □

There are _____ apples altogether.

2.

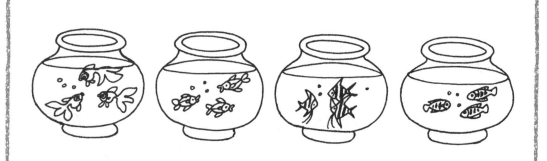

How many fish are there altogether?

□ ○ □ = □

There are _____ fish altogether.

3.

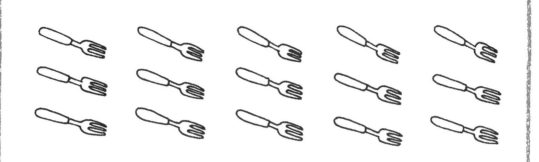

How many forks are there altogether?

There are _____ forks altogether.

4.

How many stamps are there altogether?

$$\boxed{}\bigcirc\boxed{} = \boxed{}$$

There are _____ stamps altogether.

5. Complete the multiplication equation for each picture.

(a)

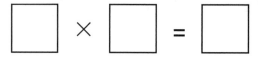

$\boxed{} \times \boxed{} = \boxed{}$

(b)

$\boxed{} \times \boxed{} = \boxed{}$

(c)

$\boxed{} \times \boxed{} = \boxed{}$

(d)

$\boxed{} \times \boxed{} = \boxed{}$

Unit 12: Multiplication

REVIEW 12

1. Complete the multiplication equations.

(a)

$$2 \times 5 =$$

(b)

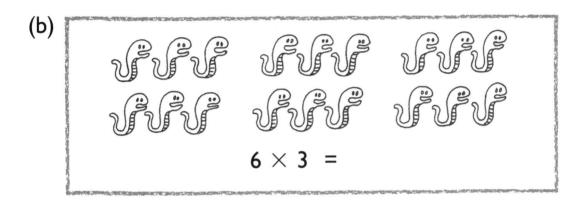

$$6 \times 3 =$$

2.

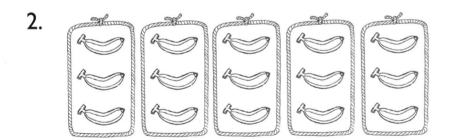

How many bananas are there altogether?

$$3 + 3 + 3 + 3 + 3 = \underline{\hspace{3cm}}$$

There are _____ bananas altogether.

3. Multiply.

(a)

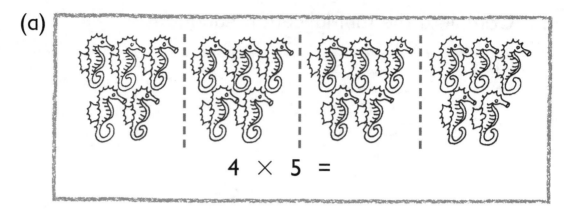

$$4 \times 5 =$$

(b)

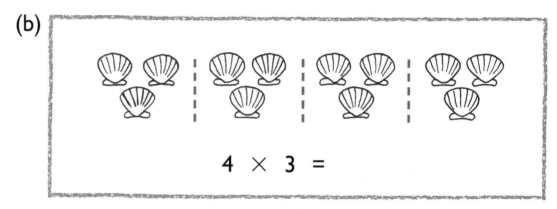

$$4 \times 3 =$$

(c)

$$3 \times 7 =$$

(d)

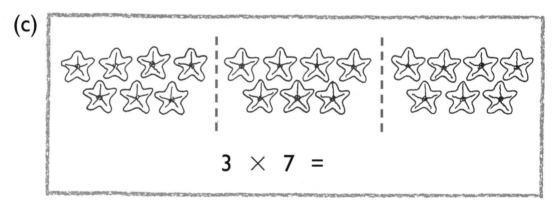

$$4 \times 6 =$$

4.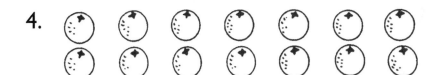

How many oranges are there altogether?

7 × 2 =

There are _____ oranges altogether.

5.

How many fish are there altogether?

3 × 4 =

There are _____ fish altogether.

6.

There are 4 bicycles.

Each bicycle has 2 wheels.

There are _____ wheels altogether.

7.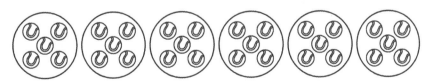

How many tennis balls are there altogether?

6 × 5 = _____

There are _____ tennis balls altogether.

EXERCISE 1

1. Fill in the blanks.

(a)

The bananas are put equally in _____ groups.

There are _____ bananas in each group.

(b)

The pears are put equally in _____ groups.

There are _____ pears in each group.

(c)

The kiwis are put equally in _____ groups.

There are _____ kiwis in each group.

2. (a)

Draw an equal number of eggs in each nest.

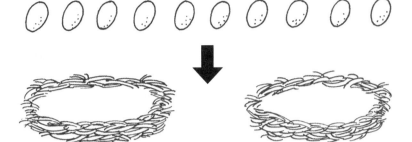

There are _____ eggs in each nest.

(b)

Draw an equal number of cupcakes on each plate.

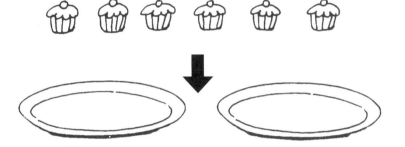

There are _____ cupcakes on each plate.

(c)

Draw an equal number of glasses on each tray.

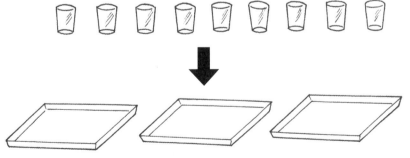

There are _____ glasses on each tray.

3.

Put 18 pears equally in 3 groups.

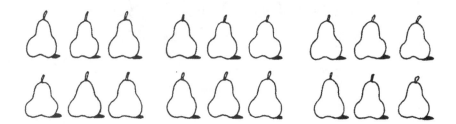

There are _____ pears in each group.

4.

Put 14 cookies equally in 2 groups.

There are _____ cookies in each group.

5.

Put 12 pencils equally in 4 groups.

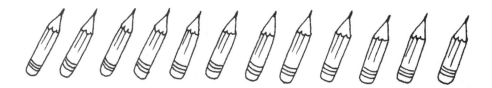

There are _____ pencils in each group.

6.

Put 16 pencils equally in 2 groups.

There are _____ pencils in each group.

7.

Put 12 flowers equally in 3 groups.

There are _____ flowers in each group.

8.

Put 15 fish equally in 3 groups.

There are _____ fish in each group.

EXERCISE 2

1.

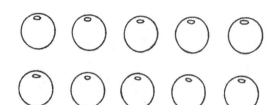 

2 girls share 10 beads equally.

How many beads does each girl get?

Each girl gets _____ beads.

2.

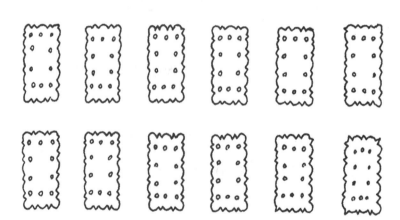

4 children share 12 crackers equally.

How many crackers does each child get?

Each child gets _____ crackers.

3.

Divide 12 picture cards into 3 equal groups.

How many picture cards are there in each group?

There are _____ picture cards in each group.

4.

There are 20 buns.

Mark wants to put 4 buns in each box.

How many boxes does he need?

He needs _____ boxes.

EXERCISE 3

1. (a)

There are 10 children.
Circle groups of 2.

There are _____ groups of 2.

(b)

There are 18 boats.
Circle groups of 3.

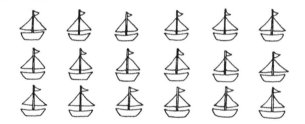

There are _____ groups of 3.

(c)

There are 24 pears.
Circle groups of 4.

There are _____ groups of 4.

2. Fill in the blanks.

(a)

There are 15 kiwis.

Kate puts 3 kiwis on each plate.

She uses _____ plates.

(b)

Lily has 18 beads.

She puts 3 beads on each string.

She uses _____ strings.

REVIEW 13

1. Fill in the blanks.

The rabbits are put equally in _____ groups.

There are _____ rabbits in each group.

2. Circle groups of 3.

There are _____ groups.

3. Put the 6 oranges equally into 2 baskets.
   Draw the oranges in the baskets.

4. Fill in the blank.

There are 12 pumpkins.

Janet puts 3 pumpkins into each basket.

She uses _____ baskets.

5. Fill in the blank.

Put the 15 flowers equally into 3 groups.

There are _____ flowers in each group.

6.

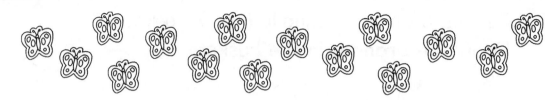

Share 15 stickers equally among 3 children.

How many stickers does each child get?

Each child gets _____ stickers.

7. Fill in the blank.

Mark has 24 buttons.

He uses 6 buttons for each shirt.

He has buttons for _____ shirts.

8.

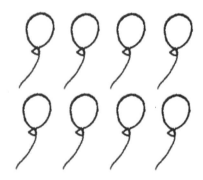

Share 8 balloons equally between 2 children.

How many balloons does each child get?

Each child gets _____ balloons.

9. Circle groups of 6 marbles.
   How many groups are there?

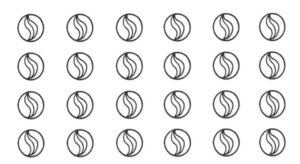

   There are _____ groups.

10.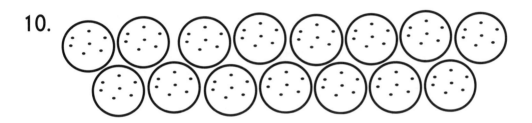

   (a) 5 children share 15 crackers equally.
       How many crackers will each child get?

       Each child will get _____ crackers.

   (b) There are 15 crackers.
       Maria wants to put 5 crackers on each plate.
       How many plates does she need?

       She needs _____ plates.

EXERCISE 1

1. Write Yes or No.

(a)

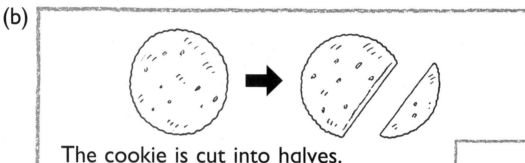

The watermelon is cut into halves.

(b)

The cookie is cut into halves.

(c)

The shaded part
shows a half of the shape.

(d)

The shaded part shows
a fourth or a quarter
of the shape.

(e)

The line divides the letter M into halves.

(f)

The line divides the letter Q into halves.

(g)

The shaded part
shows a half of the shape.

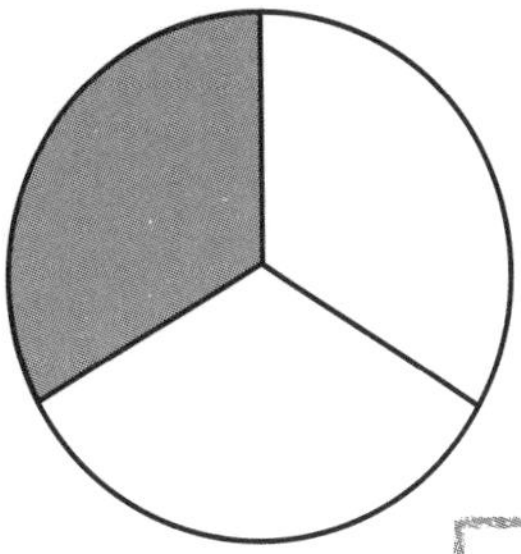

(h)

The shaded part shows
a fourth or a quarter
of the shape.

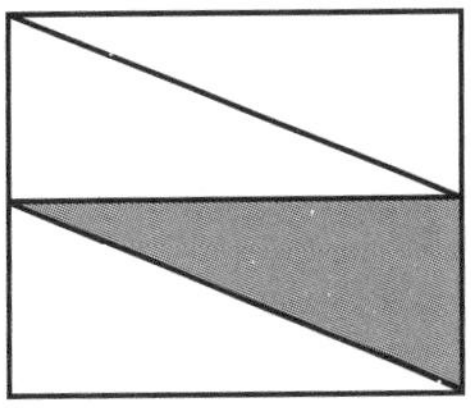

EXERCISE 2

1. Color a half of each of the following shapes.

(a)
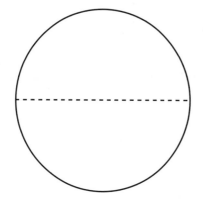

(b)
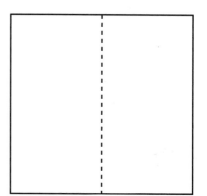

(c)
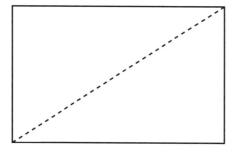

(d)
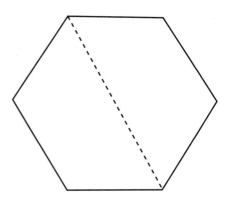

(e)
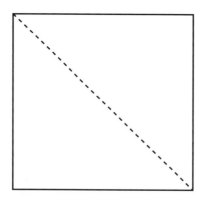

(f)
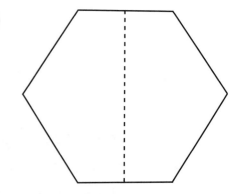

Unit 14: Halves and Fourths

2. Color a fourth of each of the following shapes.

(a)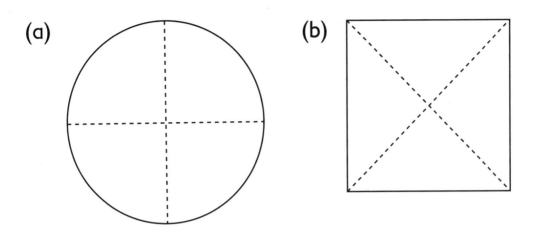

(b)

(c)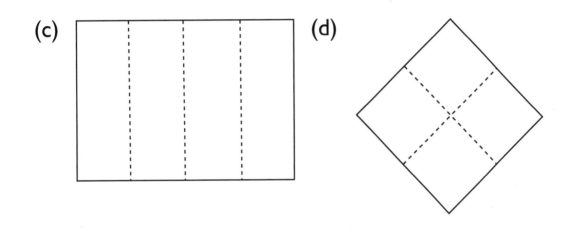

(d)

(e)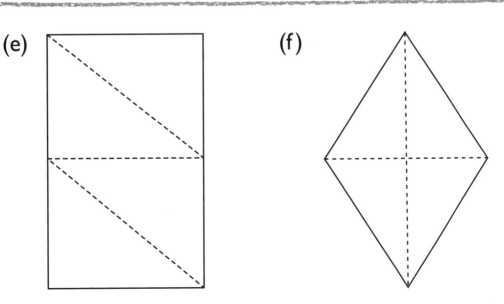

(f)

REVIEW 14

1. Check ☑ the figure that is half shaded.

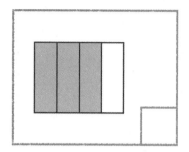 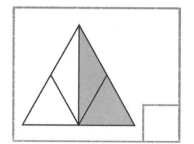

2. Write Yes or No.

(a)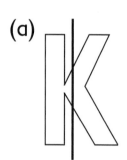

The line cuts the letter K into halves.

_____

(b)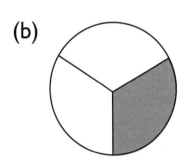

The circle is half shaded.

_____

(c)

The cake is cut into fourths.

_____

(d)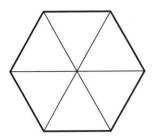

The shape is cut into quarters.

_____

3. Color one half of each figure.

(a)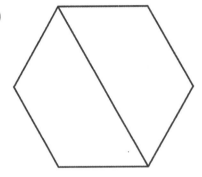

(b)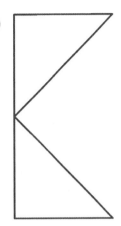

4. Color one quarter of each figure.

(a)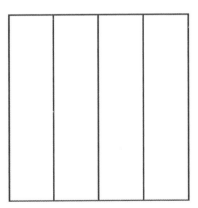

(b)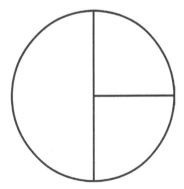

5. How many more triangle(s) need to be shaded for the rectangle to be half shaded? _____

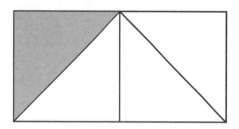

6. (a) How many halves are shaded? _____

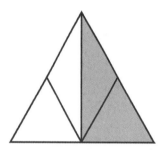

   (b) How many halves are shaded? _____

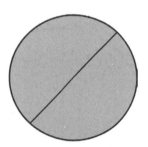

   (c) There are _____ fourths shaded.

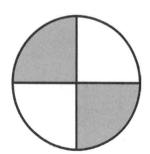

EXERCISE 1

1. Match.

8 o'clock

5 o'clock

1 o'clock

3 o'clock

11 o'clock

10 o'clock

7 o'clock

9 o'clock

2. Write the time shown on each clock.

(a)

Matthew has lunch at _____.

(b)

He does his homework at _____.

(c)

He goes swimming at _____.

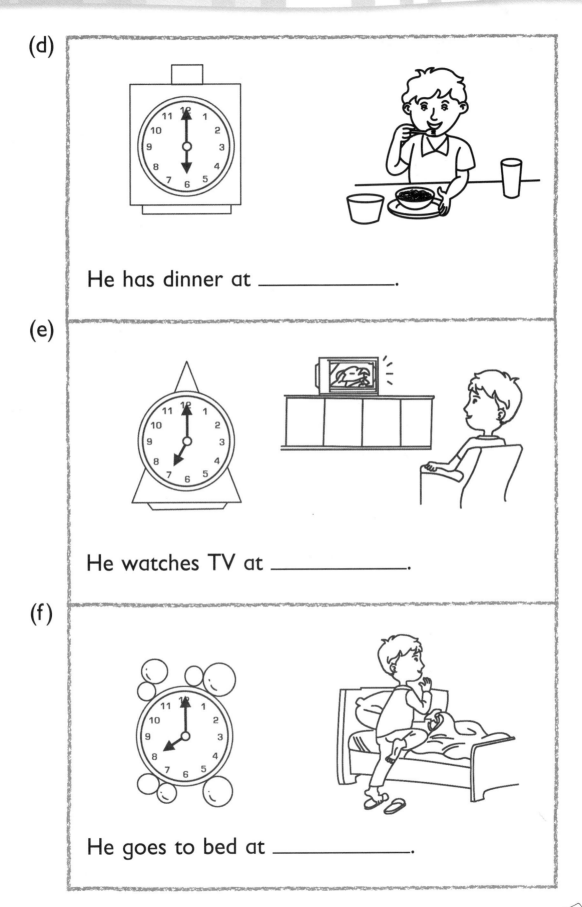

(d)

He has dinner at _____.

(e)

He watches TV at _____.

(f)

He goes to bed at _____.

EXERCISE 2

1. Match.

| half past 6 |

| two thirty |

6:30

5:00

| 6 o'clock |

| half past 7 |

| half past 10 |

| 5 o'clock |

7:30

2. Write the time shown on each clock face.

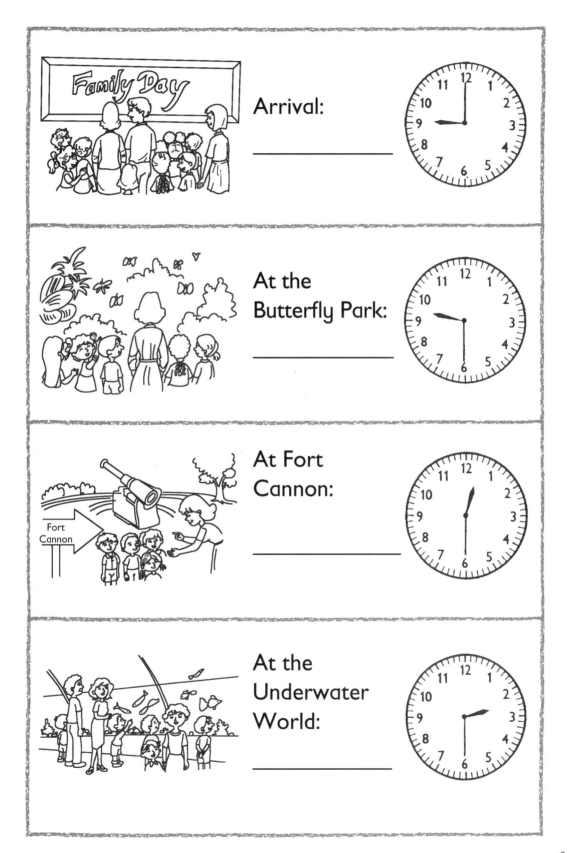

Arrival:

_____

At the Butterfly Park:

_____

At Fort Cannon:

_____

At the Underwater World:

_____

3. Write the time shown on each clock.

_____   _____

_____   _____

_____   _____

EXERCISE 3

1. Match the clocks with the correct answers.

 •   • a little after 11 o'clock

 •   • a little before 4 o'clock

 •   • about 8 o'clock

 •   • almost 3 o'clock

 •   • about half past 2

 •   • close to 6 o'clock

2. Which takes longer?

   Check ☑ the correct box.

☐   ☐

3. Which takes the longest?

   Check ☑ the correct box.

1, 2, 3, 4, 5

☐   ☐

Good morning!

☐

REVIEW 15

1. Match.

4 o'clock

half past 3

3 o'clock

half past 4

2. Complete the sentences.

(a) The time is _____ o'clock.

(b) It is half past _____.

(c) It is _____ o'clock.

3. Fill in the blank.

Nina jogs every morning at half past _____.

4. Fill in the blank.

Juan goes to bed **at almost** _____ o'clock.

5. Check ✓ the activity that takes longer.

6. Look at Emma's diary. Then complete the sentences.

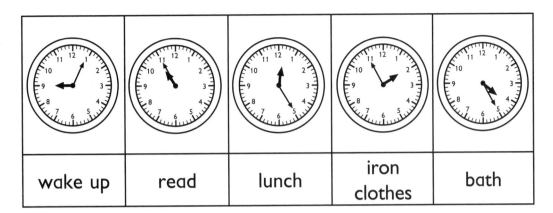

| wake up | read | lunch | iron clothes | bath |

(a) Emma wakes up a **little after** _____ o'clock.

(b) She reads the papers at **almost** _____ o'clock.

(c) She has her lunch at **about half** past _____.

(d) She irons her clothes a **little before** _____ o'clock.

(e) She takes a bath at **about half** past _____.

7. Complete the sentence.

It is a little after _____ o'clock.

8. Match the pictures to the correct times.

•   •

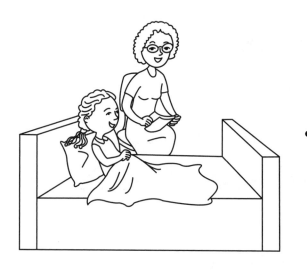 

•   •

 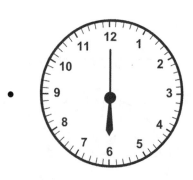

•   •

9. Match the times to the correct answers.

 •

• It is almost half past 4.

 •

• It is about half past 8.

 •

• It is almost half past 7.

 •

• It is about 7 o'clock.

 •

• It is almost 11 o'clock.

Review 15

EXERCISE 1

1. Match.

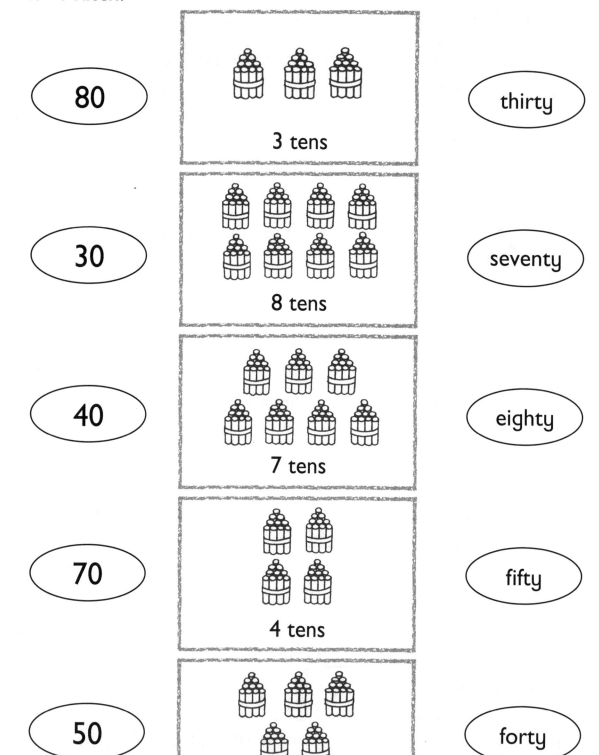

80		thirty
30	3 tens	seventy
40	8 tens	eighty
70	7 tens	fifty
50	4 tens	forty
	5 tens	

Unit 16: Numbers to 120

2. Write how many tens.
   Then write the number.

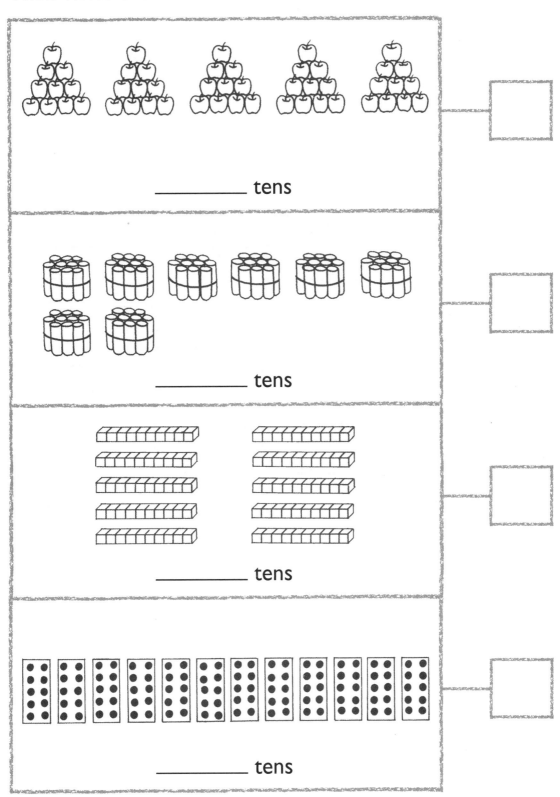

_____ tens

_____ tens

_____ tens

_____ tens

3. Write the numbers.

sixty

60

twenty

ninety

eighty

ten

thirty

fifty

one hundred

seventy

forty

EXERCISE 2

1. Match.

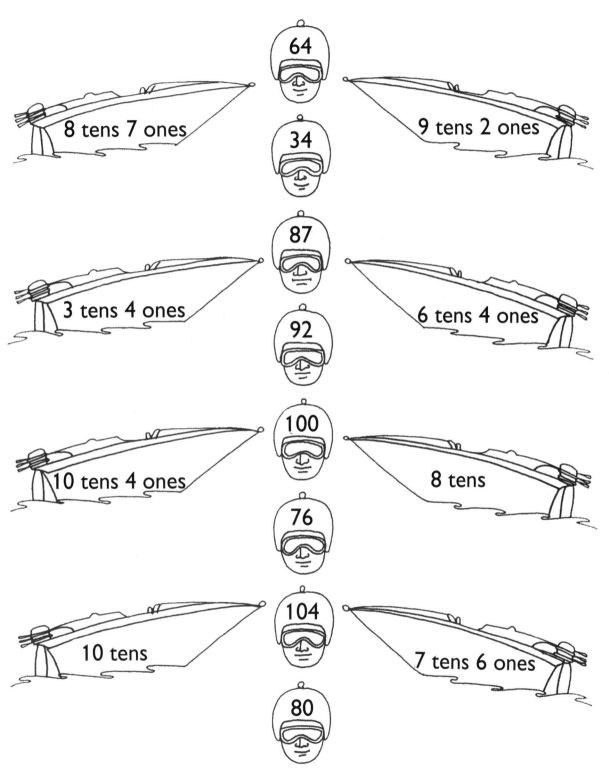

2. Color the correct number.

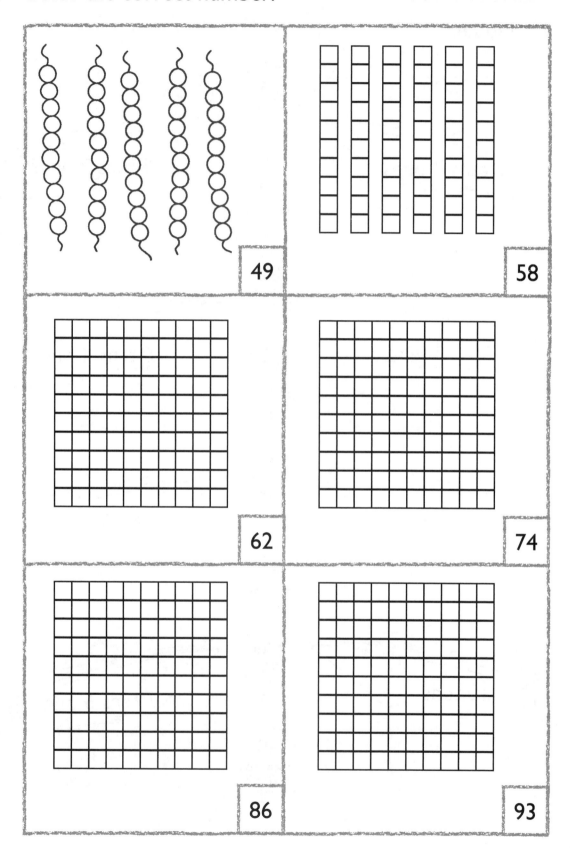

49

58

62

74

86

93

EXERCISE 3

1. Write how many tens and ones.
    Then write the number.

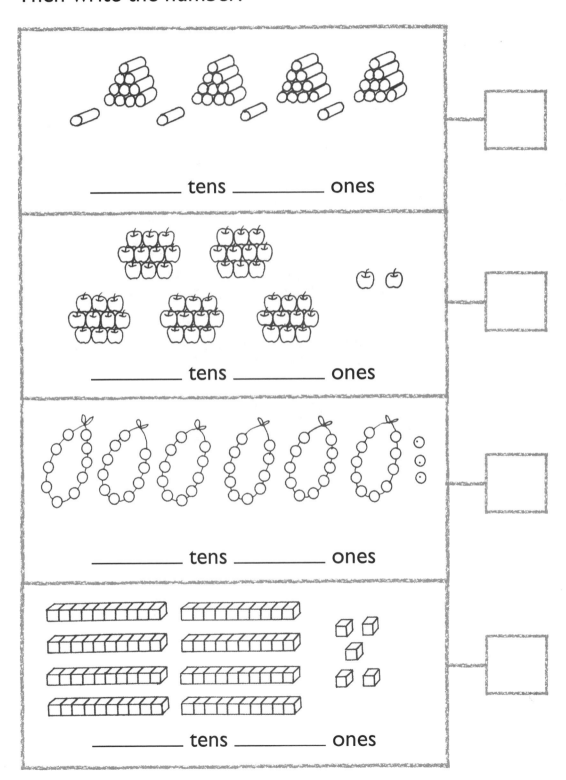

_____ tens _____ ones

_____ tens _____ ones

_____ tens _____ ones

_____ tens _____ ones

2. Write how many tens and ones.
   Then write the number.

(a)

Tens	Ones
4	6

→ 46

(b)

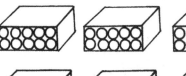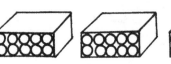

Tens	Ones

→

(c)

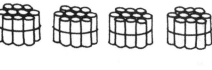

Tens	Ones

→

EXERCISE 4

1. Match.

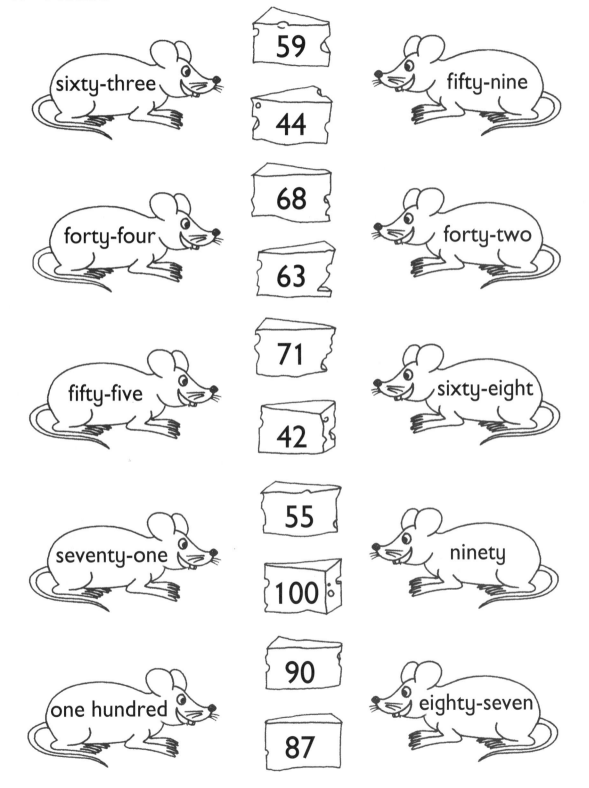

sixty-three

59

44

fifty-nine

68

forty-four

63

forty-two

71

fifty-five

42

sixty-eight

55

seventy-one

100

ninety

90

one hundred

87

eighty-seven

2. Write the numbers.

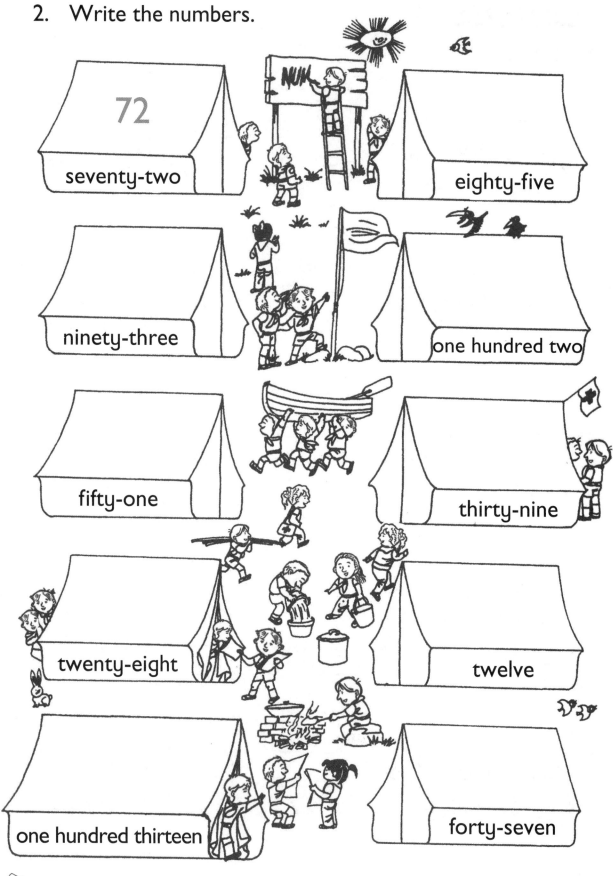

72
seventy-two

eighty-five

ninety-three

one hundred two

fifty-one

thirty-nine

twenty-eight

twelve

one hundred thirteen

forty-seven

EXERCISE 5

1. Fill in the missing numbers.

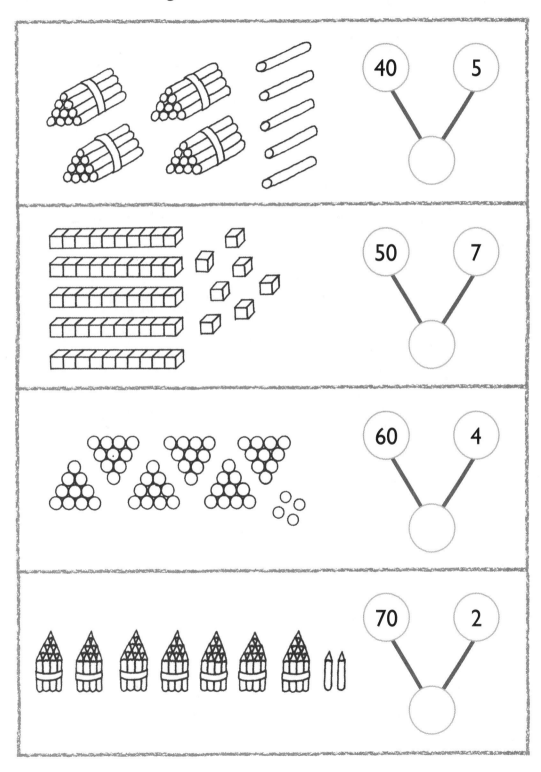

2. Add.

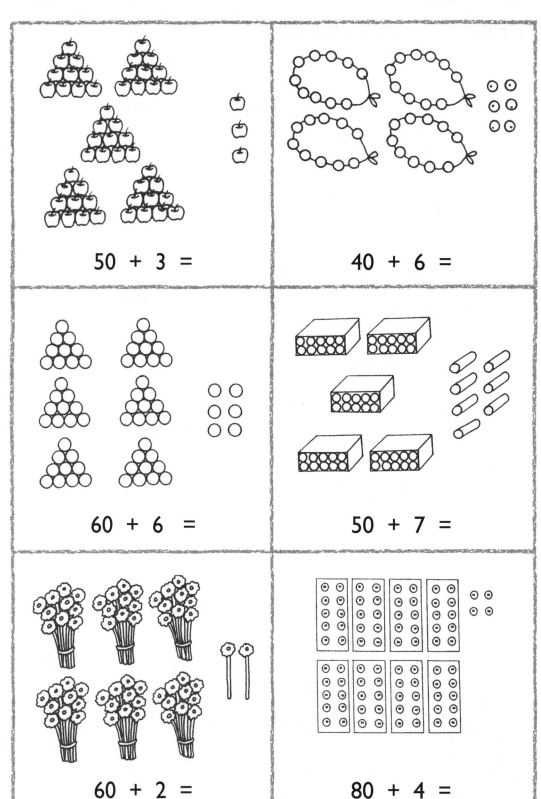

$$50 + 3 =$$

$$40 + 6 =$$

$$60 + 6 =$$

$$50 + 7 =$$

$$60 + 2 =$$

$$80 + 4 =$$

EXERCISE 6

1. Fill in the next two rows.

81	82	83	84	85	86	87	88	89	90
91	92	93	94	95	96	97	98	99	100

2. Match.

104 •   • one hundred six

115 •   • one hundred four

111 •   • one hundred fifteen

106 •   • one hundred twenty

120 •   • one hundred eleven

3. Fill in the blanks.

   (a) 10 more than 100 is _____.

   (b) 20 more than 100 is _____.

4. Fill in the blanks for the following regular number pattern.

   70, 80, _____, _____, 110, _____

EXERCISE 7

1. Estimate first, and then count.

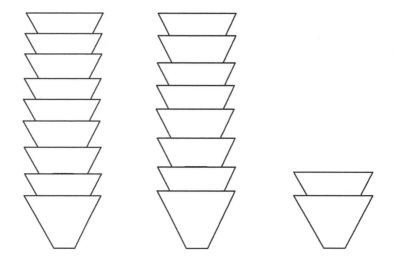

(a) There are about _____ bowls.

There are _____ bowls.

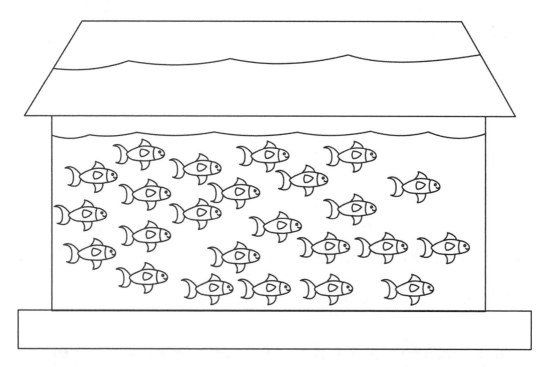

(b) There are about _____ fish in the tank.

There are _____ fish in the tank.

Unit 16: Numbers to 120

EXERCISE 8

1. Count on or count back.

   Write the missing numbers.

   (a)

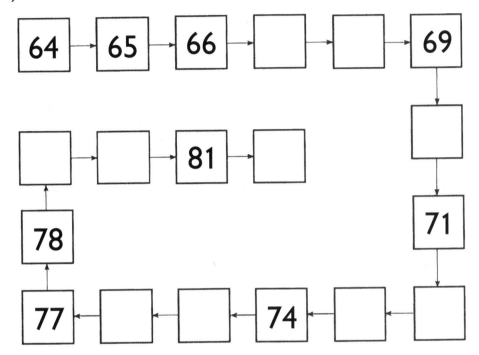

   (b)

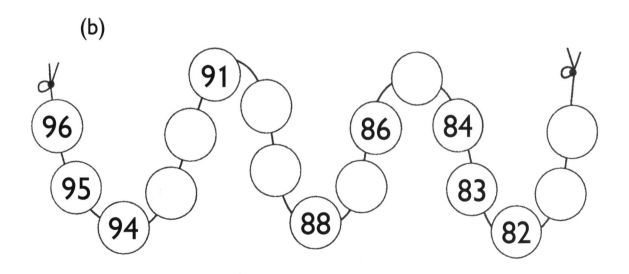

EXERCISE 9

1. Fill in the blanks.

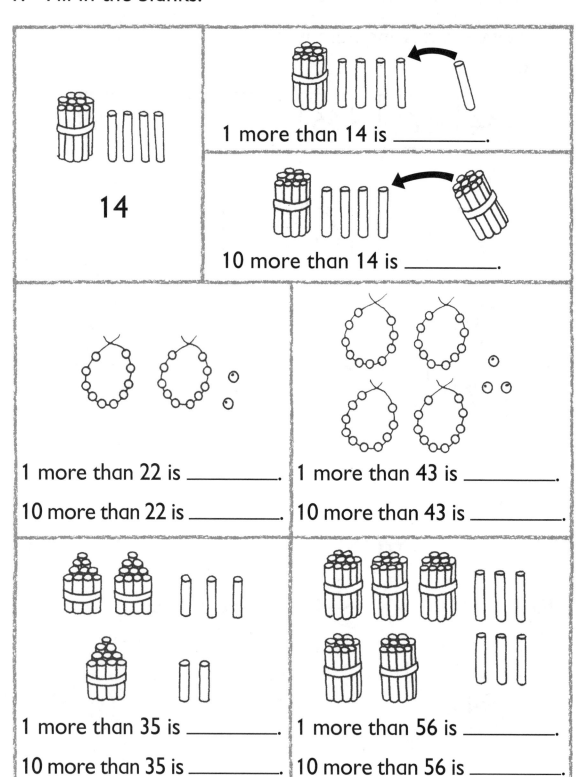

14

1 more than 14 is _____.

10 more than 14 is _____.

1 more than 22 is _____.

10 more than 22 is _____.

1 more than 43 is _____.

10 more than 43 is _____.

1 more than 35 is _____.

10 more than 35 is _____.

1 more than 56 is _____.

10 more than 56 is _____.

Unit 16: Numbers to 120

2. Fill in the blanks.

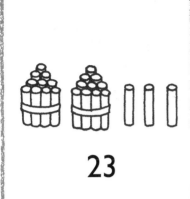

23

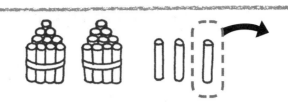

1 less than 23 is _____.

10 less than 23 is _____.

1 less than 15 is _____.

10 less than 15 is _____.

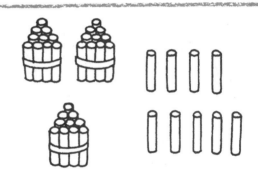

1 less than 39 is _____.

10 less than 39 is _____.

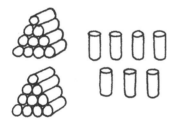

1 less than 27 is _____.

10 less than 27 is _____.

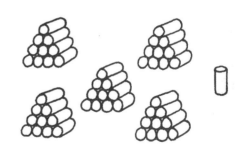

1 less than 51 is _____.

10 less than 51 is _____.

EXERCISE 10

1. Follow the arrows and fill in the missing numbers.

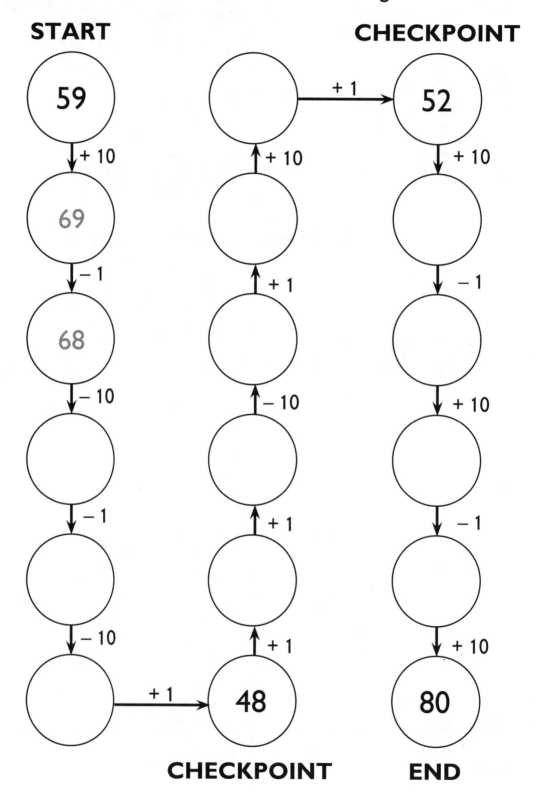

START

CHECKPOINT

59

+ 10

69

− 1

68

− 10

− 1

− 10

+ 1

+ 1

48

+ 1

+ 1

+ 10

− 10

+ 1

+ 10

+ 1

52

+ 10

− 1

+ 10

− 1

+ 10

80

CHECKPOINT

END

EXERCISE 11

1. Complete the equations.

1	2	3	4	5	6	7	8	9	10
11	12	13	14	15	16	17	18	19	20
21	22	23	24	25	26	27	28	29	30
31	32	33	34	35	36	37	38	39	40
41	42	43	44	45	46	47	48	49	50
51	52	53	54	55	56	57	58	59	60
61	62	63	64	65	66	67	68	69	70
71	72	73	74	75	76	77	78	79	80
81	82	83	84	85	86	87	88	89	90
91	92	93	94	95	96	97	98	99	100

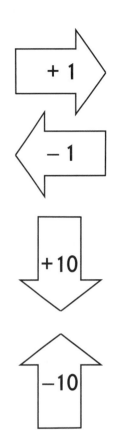

$+ 1$

$- 1$

$+10$

-10

(a) $45 + 10 =$ ☐

Count on 1 ten from 45.

(b) $39 + 30 =$ ☐

Count on 3 tens from 39.

(c) $95 - 20 =$ ☐

Count back 2 tens from 95.

Unit 16: Numbers to 120

(d) 68 − 2 = ☐

Count back
2 ones from 68.

(e) 71 + 3 = ☐

Count on 3 ones
from 71.

(f) 56 − 30 = ☐

Count back
3 tens from 56.

(g) 87 − 3 = ☐

Count back
3 ones from 87.

(h) 64 + 20 = ☐

Count on 2 tens
from 64.

EXERCISE 12

1. Fill in the blanks.

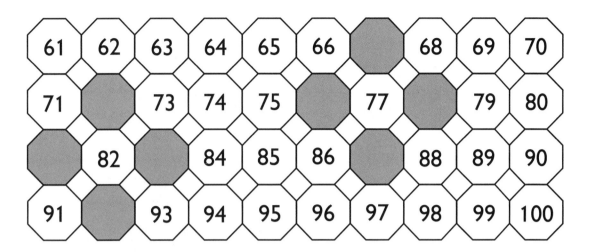

(a) 1 more than 77 is _____.

(b) 10 more than 77 is _____.

(c) 1 less than 82 is _____.

(d) 10 less than 82 is _____.

(e) 1 more than 80 is _____.

(f) 2 less than 80 is _____.

(g) 3 less than 84 is _____.

(h) 10 less than 86 is _____.

(i) 20 less than 98 is _____.

(j) 30 more than 62 is _____.

(k) 20 less than 96 is _____.

EXERCISE 13

1. Circle the greater number.

(a)
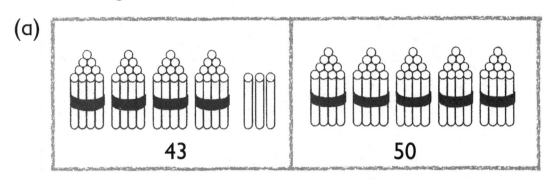
43   50

(b)
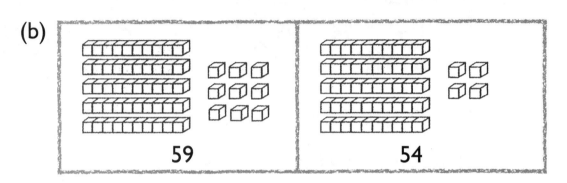
59   54

(c) 28   26   (d) 70   65

(e) 78   87   (f) 99   100

2. Circle the greatest number.

(a) 43   45   42   (b) 78   87   85

(c) 63   60   62   (d) 98   99   100

(e) 59   70   62   (f) 57   52   54

3. Circle the smaller number.

(a)
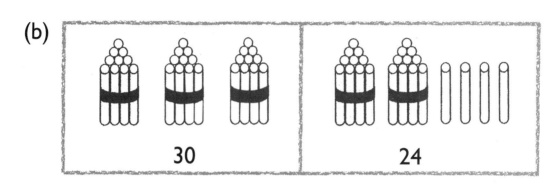

| 23 | 25 |

(b)

| 30 | 24 |

(c) 31   29   (d) 78   87

(e) 54   57   (f) 89   87

(g) 63   60   (h) 98   100

4. Circle the smallest number.

(a) 35   31   32   (b) 54   50   59

(c) 45   50   47   (d) 59   56   66

(e) 15   23   26   (f) 38   40   36

5. (a) Arrange the numbers in order.
   Begin with the smallest.

☐—☐—☐—☐

(b) Arrange the numbers in order.
    Begin with the greatest.

☐—☐—☐—☐

6. Write **>** (greater than) or **<** (less than).

(a) 44 ◯ 40

(b) 50 ◯ 65

(c) 62 ◯ 61

(d) 70 ◯ 77

(e) 39 ◯ 49

(f) 58 ◯ 57

(g) 73 ◯ 69

(h) 65 ◯ 66

(i) 24 ◯ 30

(j) 47 ◯ 39

Unit 16: Numbers to 120

7. Write the numbers in order.
   Begin with the given number.

12 36 43 17	12 ◯ ◯ ◯ The smallest number is _____. The greatest number is _____.
29 50 52 38	52 ☐ ☐ ☐ The smallest number is _____. The greatest number is _____.
93 84 68 86	93 △ △ △ The smallest number is _____. The greatest number is _____.
60 95 72 58	58 ☐ ☐ ☐ The smallest number is _____. The greatest number is _____.

EXERCISE 14

1. Add.

(a)

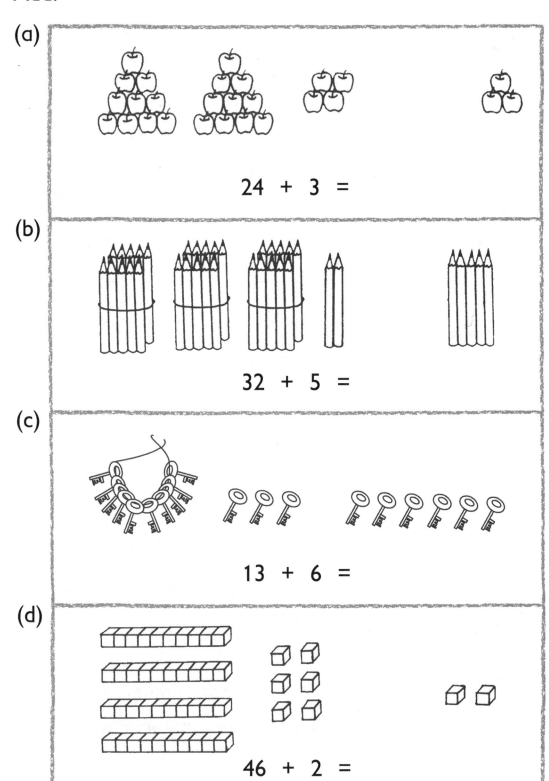

24 + 3 =

(b)

32 + 5 =

(c)

13 + 6 =

(d)

46 + 2 =

2. Add.

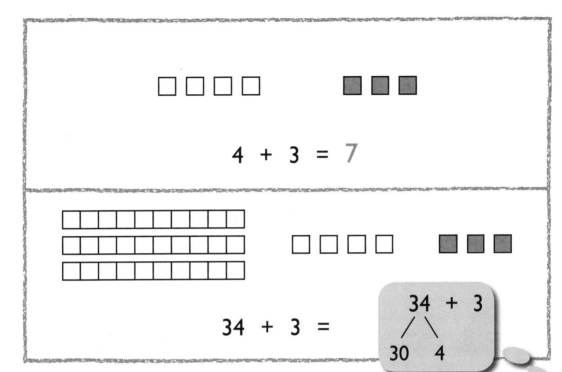

$$4 + 3 = 7$$

$$34 + 3 =$$

34 + 3
/ \
30   4

5 + 2 = 25 + 2 =	6 + 1 = 36 + 1 =
4 + 4 = 44 + 4 =	7 + 2 = 57 + 2 =
3 + 3 = 63 + 3 =	1 + 8 = 71 + 8 =

EXERCISE 15

1. Add.

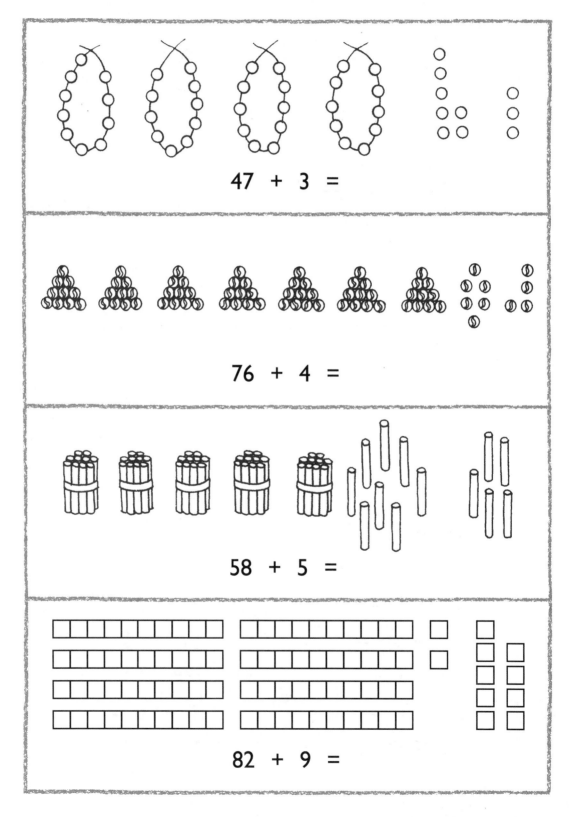

47 + 3 =

76 + 4 =

58 + 5 =

82 + 9 =

2. Add.

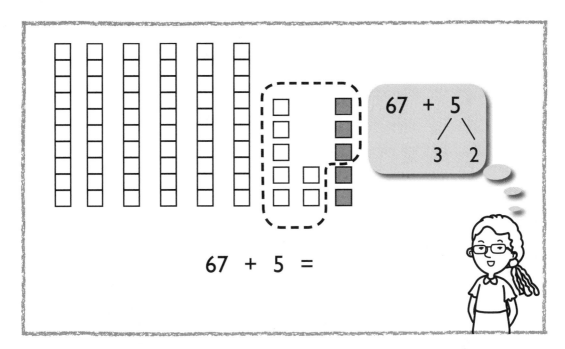

67 + 5 =

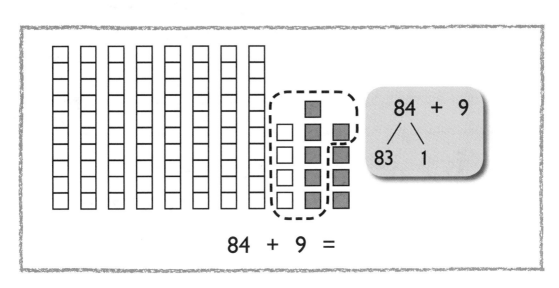

84 + 9 =

63 + 7 =	29 + 7 =
34 + 6 =	88 + 9 =
55 + 8 =	94 + 6 =

3. Add.

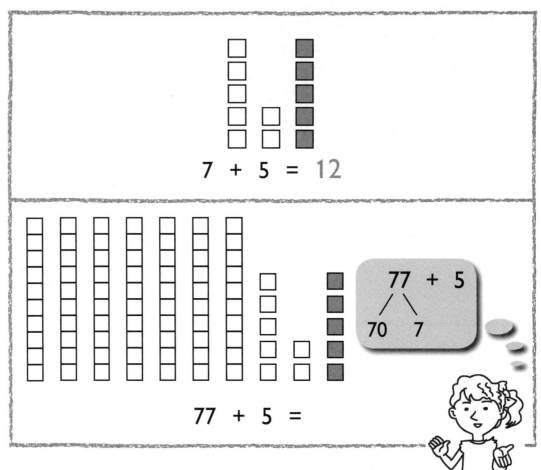

$7 + 5 = 12$

$77 + 5 =$

$77 + 5$
$70 \quad 7$

$5 + 5 =$ $45 + 5 =$	$4 + 7 =$ $64 + 7 =$
$6 + 8 =$ $86 + 8 =$	$9 + 4 =$ $59 + 4 =$
$5 + 6 =$ $75 + 6 =$	$8 + 2 =$ $68 + 2 =$

EXERCISE 16

1. Add.

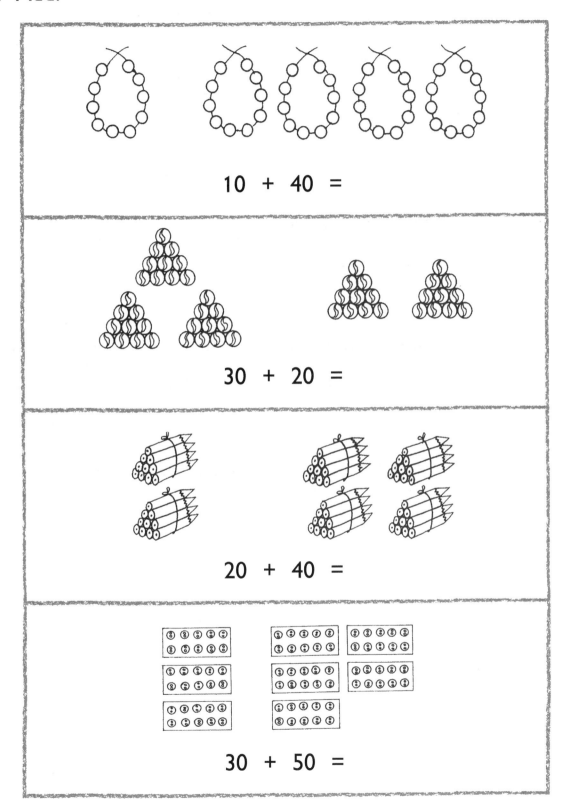

10 + 40 =

30 + 20 =

20 + 40 =

30 + 50 =

2. Add.

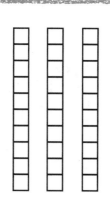 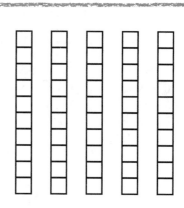

3 tens + 5 tens = _____ tens

30 + 50 = _____

2 tens + 3 tens = _____ tens

20 + 30 = _____

1 ten + 5 tens = _____ tens

10 + 50 = _____

3 tens + 4 tens = _____ tens

30 + 40 = _____

6 tens + 2 tens = _____ tens

60 + 20 = _____

2 tens + 7 tens = _____ tens

20 + 70 = _____

3 tens + 3 tens = _____ tens

30 + 30 = _____

8 tens + 1 ten = _____ tens

80 + 10 = _____

5 tens + 4 tens = _____ tens

50 + 40 = _____

EXERCISE 17

1. Add.

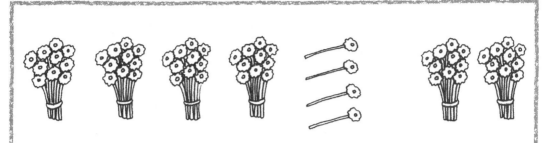

44 + 20 =

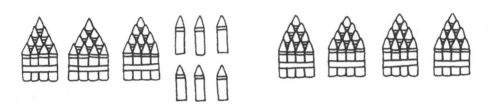

36 + 40 =

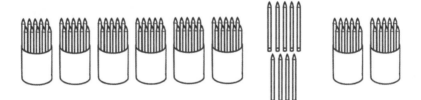

69 + 20 =

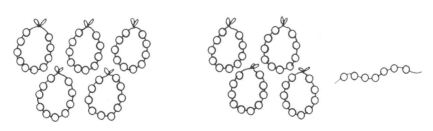

50 + 47 =

2. Add.

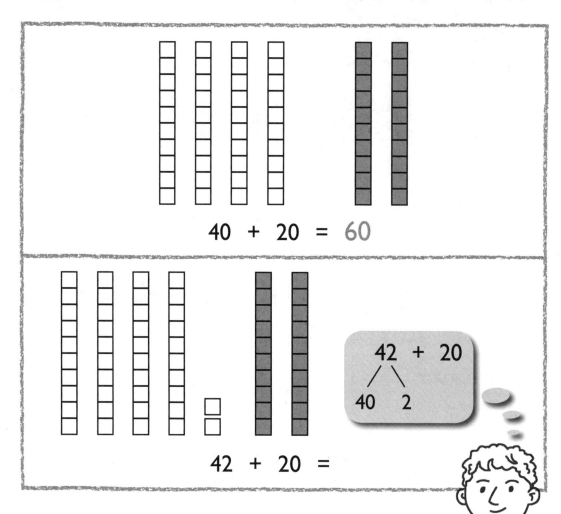

40 + 20 = 60

42 + 20 =

42 + 20
40   2

40 + 30 =	20 + 70 =
40 + 36 =	28 + 70 =
10 + 60 =	50 + 30 =
17 + 60 =	50 + 35 =
50 + 20 =	20 + 60 =
54 + 20 =	21 + 60 =

EXERCISE 18

1. Add.

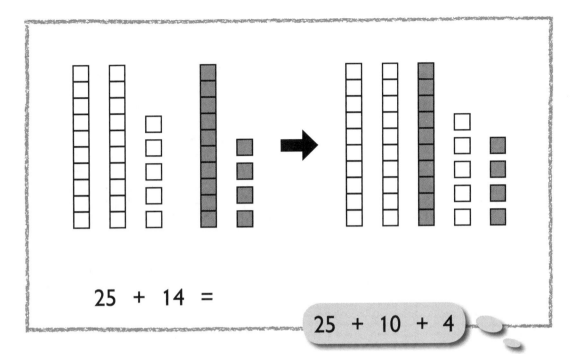

$$25 \ + \ 14 \ =$$

$$25 \ + \ 10 \ + \ 4$$

$45 \ + \ 10 \ + \ 3 \ =$ $45 \ + \ 13 \ =$	$24 \ + \ 10 \ + \ 2 \ =$ $24 \ + \ 12 \ =$
$37 \ + \ 10 \ + \ 3 \ =$ $37 \ + \ 13 \ =$	$76 \ + \ 10 \ + \ 4 \ =$ $76 \ + \ 14 \ =$
$25 \ + \ 10 \ + \ 7 \ =$ $25 \ + \ 17 \ =$	$48 \ + \ 10 \ + \ 6 \ =$ $48 \ + \ 16 \ =$

2. Add.

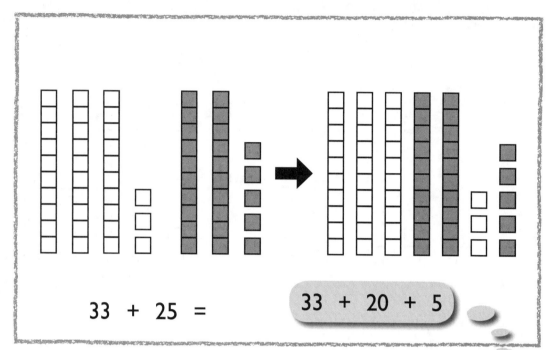

33 + 25 =

33 + 20 + 5

42 + 30 + 6 = 42 + 36 =	35 + 40 + 2 = 35 + 42 =
55 + 20 + 5 = 55 + 25 =	28 + 60 + 2 = 28 + 62 =
37 + 30 + 8 = 37 + 38 =	65 + 20 + 9 = 65 + 29 =

3. Add.

(a) 33 + 33 =	(b) 41 + 13 =
(c) 37 + 12 =	(d) 25 + 21 =
(e) 62 + 21 =	(f) 70 + 29 =

4. Add.

(a) 53 + 37 =	(b) 45 + 52 =
(c) 37 + 25 =	(d) 64 + 17 =
(e) 69 + 24 =	(f) 55 + 36 =

EXERCISE 19

1. Subtract.

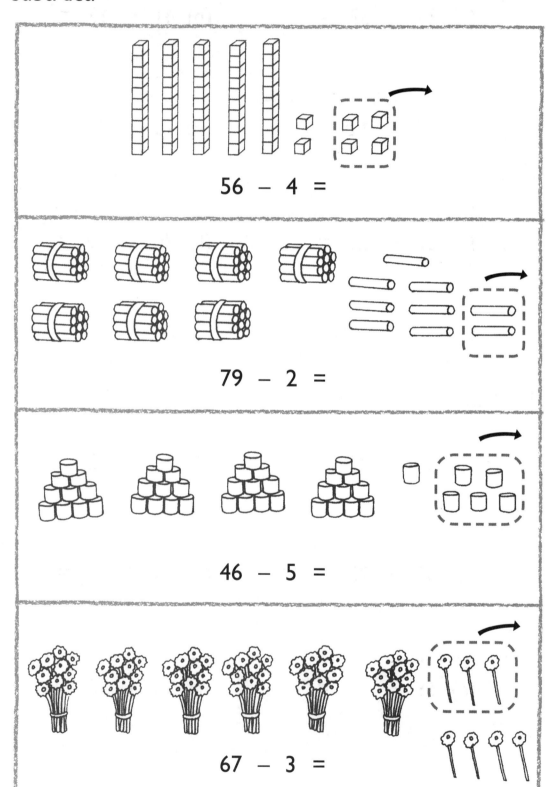

56 – 4 =

79 – 2 =

46 – 5 =

67 – 3 =

2. Subtract.

$$7 - 3 = 4$$

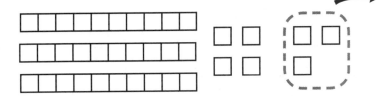

$$37 - 3 =$$

$$37 - 3$$
$$30 \quad 7$$

$5 - 3 =$ $65 - 3 =$	$8 - 5 =$ $78 - 5 =$
$6 - 2 =$ $86 - 2 =$	$7 - 4 =$ $37 - 4 =$
$8 - 6 =$ $58 - 6 =$	$9 - 5 =$ $69 - 5 =$

EXERCISE 20

1. Subtract.

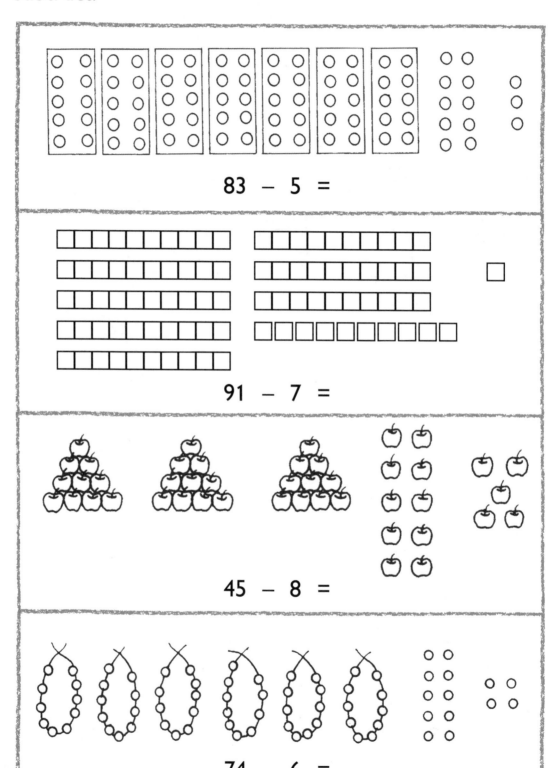

$$83 - 5 =$$

$$91 - 7 =$$

$$45 - 8 =$$

$$74 - 6 =$$

2. Subtract.

$65 - 8 =$

$84 - 9 =$

$63 - 7 =$	$29 - 9 =$
$34 - 6 =$	$88 - 9 =$
$55 - 8 =$	$94 - 5 =$

3. Subtract.

$$16 - 8 = 8$$

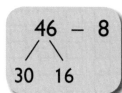

$$46 - 8 =$$

14 – 7 =	13 – 5 =
54 – 7 =	63 – 5 =
11 – 5 =	14 – 9 =
61 – 5 =	74 – 9 =
12 – 7 =	13 – 6 =
82 – 7 =	93 – 6 =

EXERCISE 21

1. Subtract.

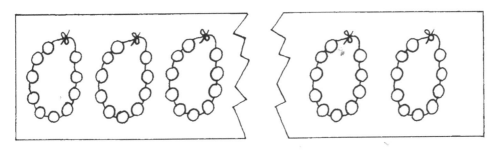

$$50 - 20 =$$

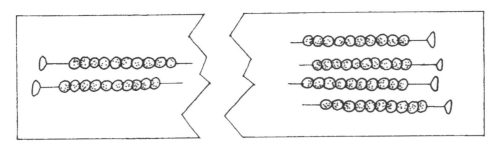

$$60 - 40 =$$

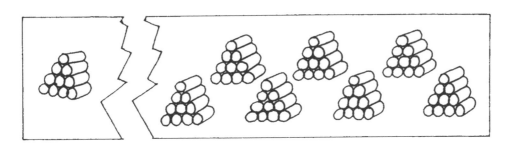

$$80 - 70 =$$

$$100 - 50 =$$

2. Subtract.

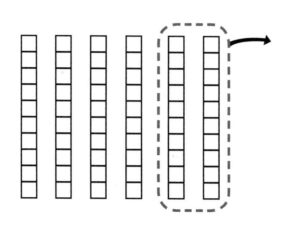

6 tens − 2 tens =

60 − 20 =

4 tens − 1 ten = _____ tens

40 − 10 = _____

5 tens − 3 tens = _____ tens

50 − 30 = _____

6 tens − 5 tens = _____ ten

60 − 50 = _____

7 tens − 4 tens = _____ tens

70 − 40 = _____

8 tens − 6 tens = _____ tens

80 − 60 = _____

7 tens − 2 tens = _____ tens

70 − 20 = _____

9 tens − 4 tens = _____ tens

90 − 40 = _____

10 tens − 7 tens = _____ tens

100 − 70 = _____

EXERCISE 22

1. Subtract.

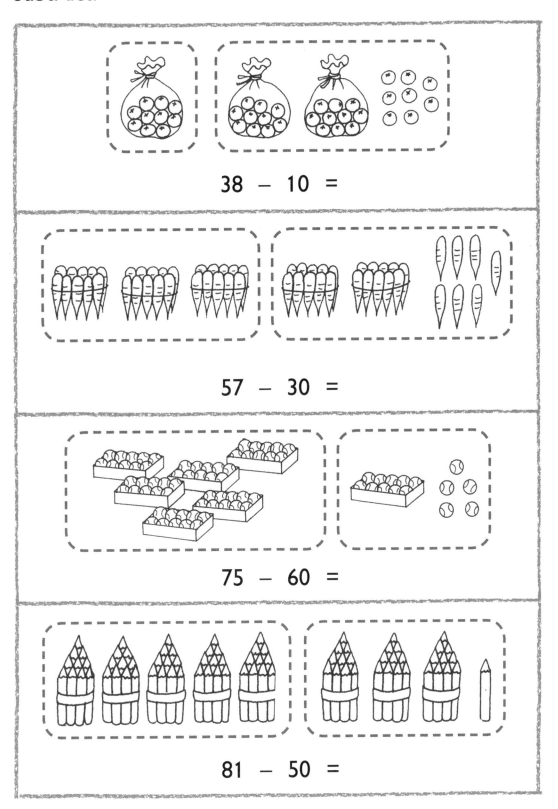

38 − 10 =

57 − 30 =

75 − 60 =

81 − 50 =

2. Subtract.

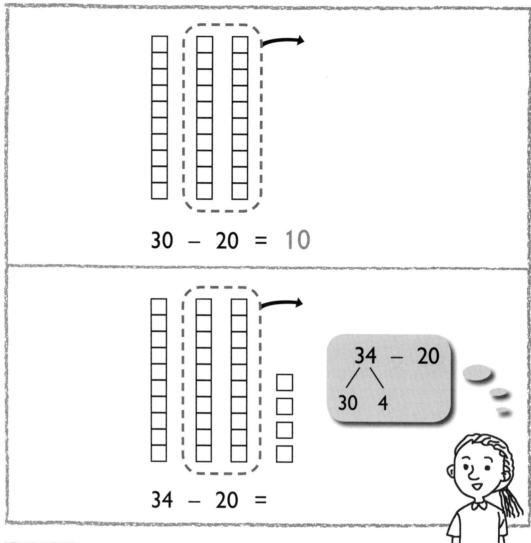

$$30 - 20 = 10$$

$$34 - 20 =$$

$$34 - 20$$
$$30 \quad 4$$

$40 - 30 =$	$60 - 20 =$
$49 - 30 =$	$62 - 20 =$
$30 - 10 =$	$80 - 40 =$
$36 - 10 =$	$83 - 40 =$
$50 - 40 =$	$90 - 80 =$
$57 - 40 =$	$95 - 80 =$

EXERCISE 23

1. Subtract.

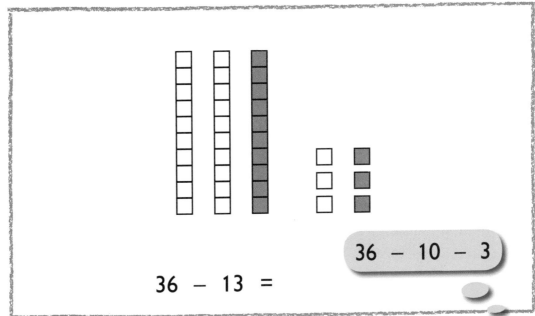

36 − 13 =

36 − 10 − 3

47 − 10 − 2 = 47 − 12 =	67 − 10 − 5 = 67 − 15 =
58 − 10 − 8 = 58 − 18 =	60 − 10 − 4 = 60 − 14 =
43 − 10 − 7 = 43 − 17 =	61 − 10 − 3 = 61 − 13 =

2. Subtract.

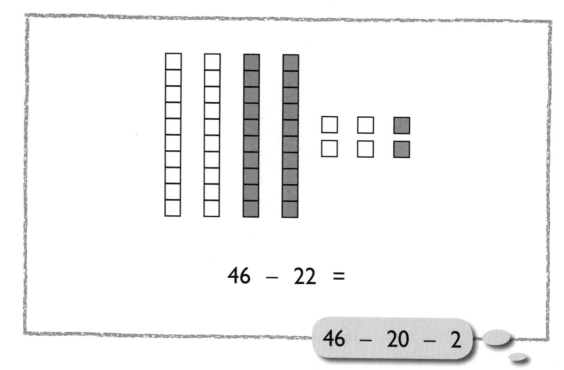

$$46 - 22 = $$

$$46 - 20 - 2$$

$68 - 20 - 4 =$ $68 - 24 =$	$75 - 40 - 2 =$ $75 - 42 =$
$53 - 30 - 3 =$ $53 - 33 =$	$60 - 20 - 8 =$ $60 - 28 =$
$73 - 40 - 7 =$ $73 - 47 =$	$96 - 80 - 7 =$ $96 - 87 =$

3. Subtract.

(a) 47 − 21 =	(b) 54 − 13 =
(c) 49 − 23 =	(d) 37 − 17 =
(e) 62 − 20 =	(f) 74 − 32 =

4. Subtract.

(a) 48 − 28 =	(b) 55 − 16 =
(c) 46 − 28 =	(d) 67 − 43 =
(e) 75 − 37 =	(f) 96 − 83 =

Unit 16: Numbers to 120

REVIEW 16

1. Count the tens and ones.

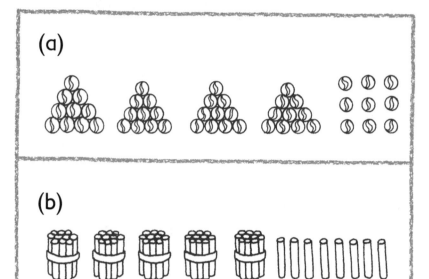

(a)

Tens	Ones

(b)

Tens	Ones

2. Fill in the blanks.

   (a) 50 and 4 make _____.

   (b) 60 and 5 make _____.

   (c) $70 + 4 =$ _____

   (d) $80 + 7 =$ _____

   (e) $90 + 8 =$ _____

3. Arrange these numbers in order.
   Begin with the smallest.

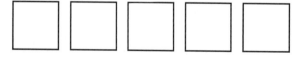

   smallest

4. Container A has about 20 peas.

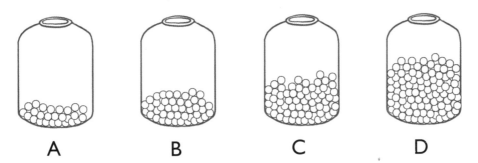

(a) Container B has about _____ peas.

(b) Container C has about _____ peas.

(c) Container D has about _____ peas.

5. Fill in the blank.

   1 more than 119 is _____.

6. Follow the arrows and fill in the missing numbers.

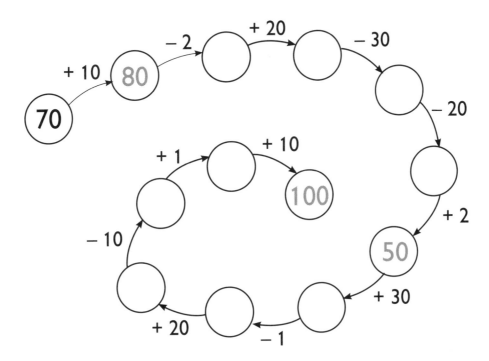

7. Add or subtract.

(a)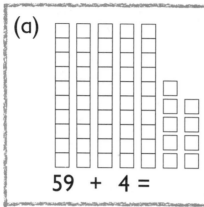
59 + 4 =

(b)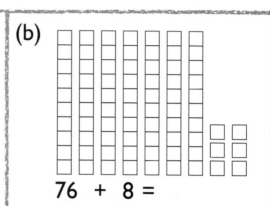
76 + 8 =

(c)
62 − 5 =

(d)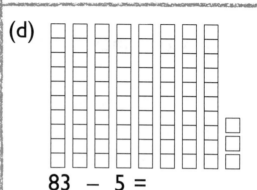
83 − 5 =

8. Fill in the blanks.

(a) 37 + 28 is the same as 37 + _____ + 8.

(b) 42 + 12 is the same as 42 + 10 + _____.

(c) 24 + _____ is the same as 24 + 30 + 6.

9. Write > (greater than) or < (less than).

(a) 4 ◯ 9

(b) 20 ◯ 2

(c) 15 ◯ 66

(d) 98 ◯ 89

(e) 77 ◯ 75

(f) 55 ◯ 65

(g) 45 ◯ 54

(h) 100 ◯ 10

EXERCISE 1

1. Match.

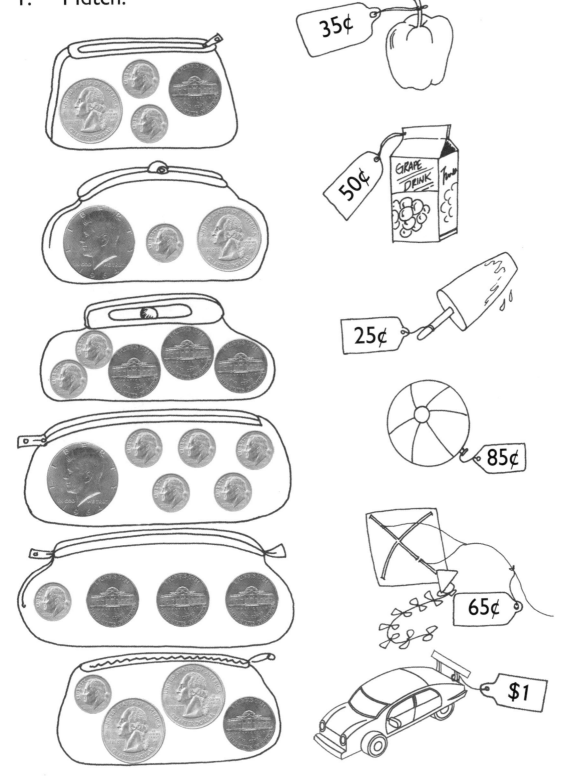

2. How much money is there in each set of coins?

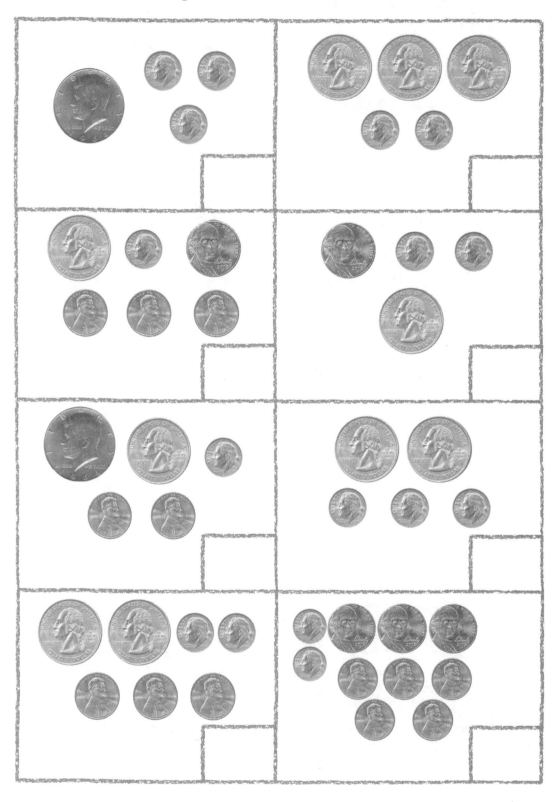

EXERCISE 2

1. Match.

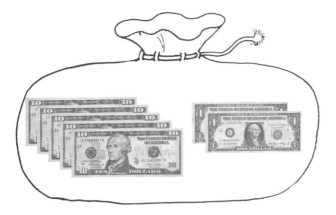 

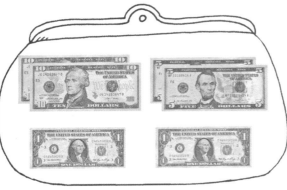 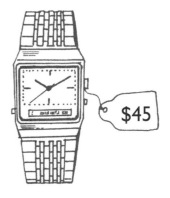

2. Color the correct amount of money.

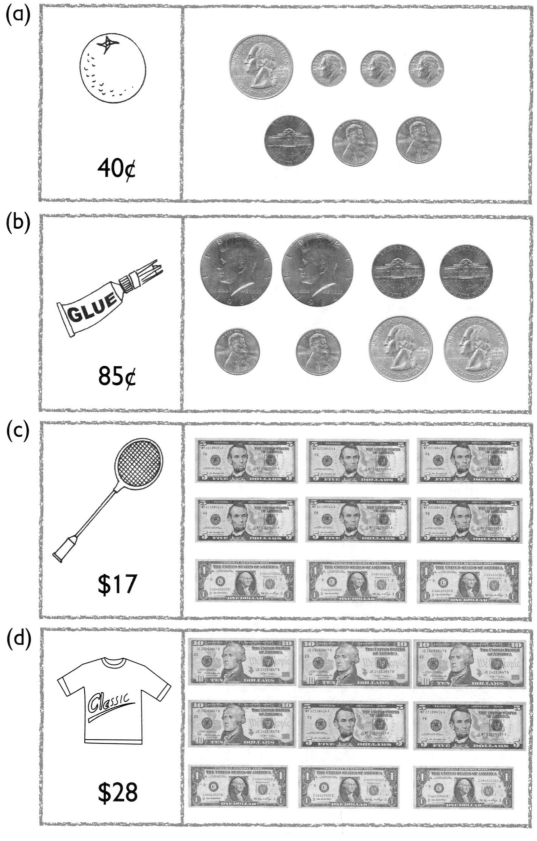

(a) 40¢

(b) 85¢

(c) $17

(d) $28

EXERCISE 3

1. Check ✓ the set that has more money.

(a)

(b)

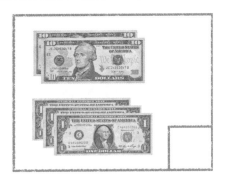

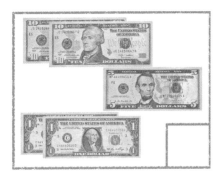

2. Check ✓ the set that has less money.

(a)

(b)

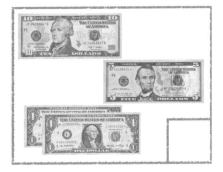

3. Check ✓ the set that has the most money.

4. Check ✓ the set that has the least money.

Unit 17: Money

EXERCISE 4

1. Is the amount of money enough to buy the item?
    Write Yes or No.

(a)

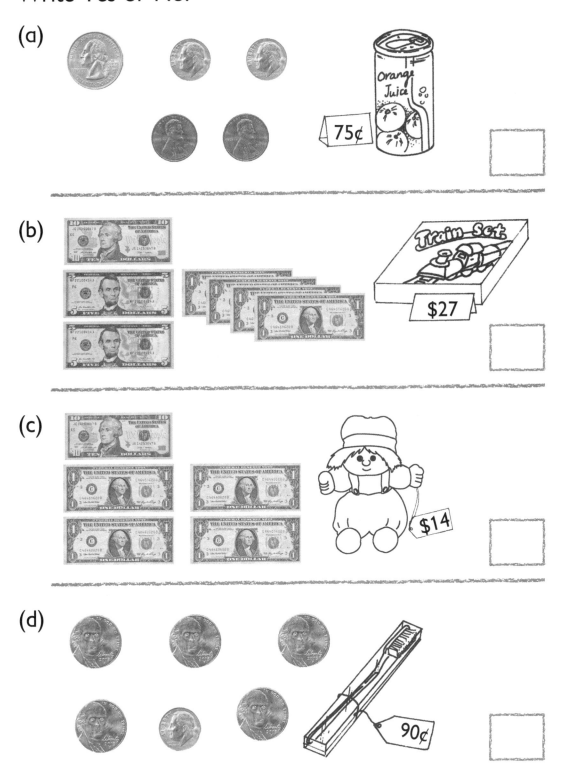

(b)

(c)

(d)

2. Mr. Brown has $20.
    He buys the watch.
    How much money does he have left?

$13

$20 − $13 =

He has $_____ left.

3.

$12

Juan has $9.
He wants to buy the toy camera.
How much more money does he need?

$12 − $9 =

He needs $_____ more.

4. Fill in the blanks.

(a) Dina has 55¢.

She wants to buy the pen.

She needs _____¢ more.

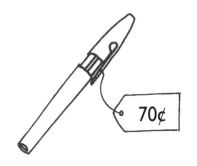

(b) Morgan has $1.

She buys the toy boat.

She has _____¢ left.

40¢ each

(c) Sara buys two pears.

She pays _____¢.

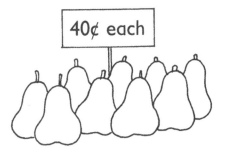

Ice cream

65¢

(d) Brian spends $1.

He buys the _____ and

the _____.

Cake

Apple

45¢

35¢

REVIEW 17

1. Match the coins to the correct value.

5 cents ●	● penny
25 cents ●	● nickel
1 cent ●	● dime
10 cents ●	● quarter

2. Fill in the blanks.

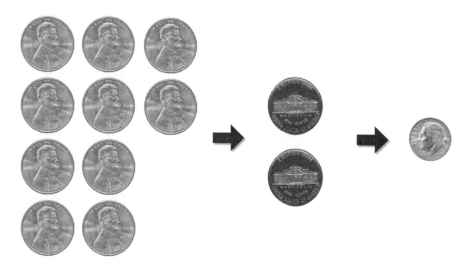

10 pennies can be changed for _____ nickels

or _____ dime.

3. Match.

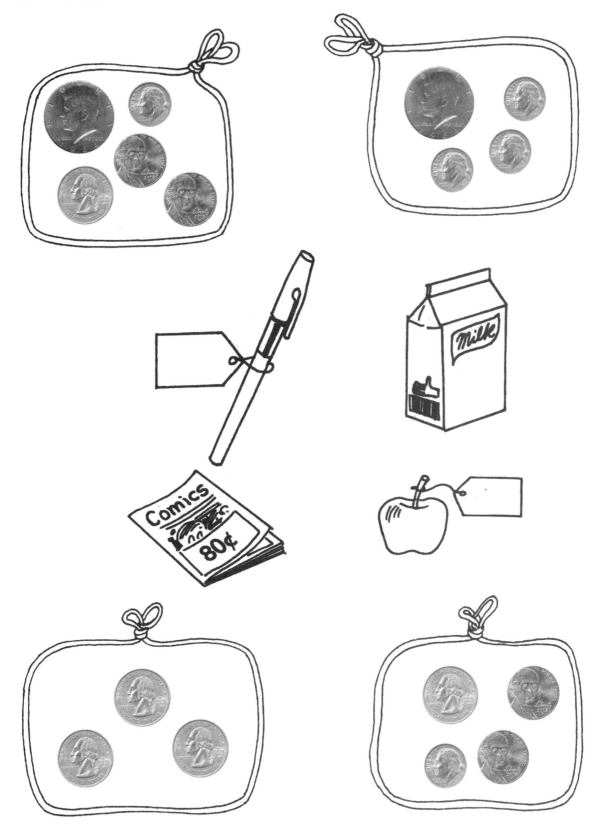

4. How much money is there in each set?

(a)

(b)

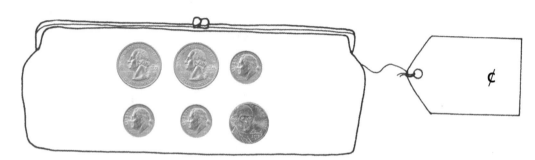

(c)

5.

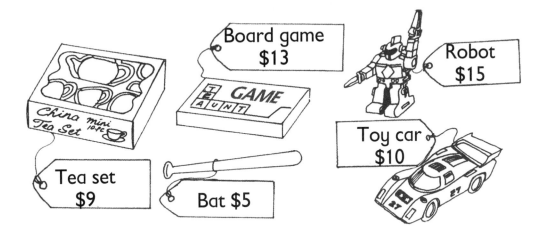

(a) Which is cheaper, the tea set or the board game?
How much cheaper?

□ ○ □ = □

The _____ is $_____ cheaper

than the _____.

(b) Ali has $12.
He wants to buy the robot.
How much more money does he need?

□ ○ □ = □

He needs $_____ more.

(c) Pablo bought the bat and the toy car.
How much did he pay?

□ ○ □ = □

He paid $_____.

6. Fill in the blanks.

Set A

Set B

(a) Set A has _____ cents.

(b) Set B has _____ dollars.

(c) Set _____ has more money.

7. Fill in the blank.

T-shirt $5

Toy guitar $8

Umbrella $6

Toy car $18

School bag $10

(a) Tara bought the toy guitar and the umbrella.

She spent $_____ altogether.

(b) Rory had $20.

He bought the toy car.

He had $_____ left.

(c) The school bag is $_____ cheaper than the toy car.

(d) Mia spent $13.

She bought the _____ and the _____.

8. Fill in the blank.

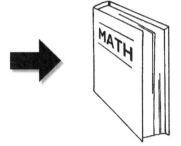

The book costs $_____.

9. Sara had $40.
   She had $6 left after buying a teddy bear.
   How much did she pay for the teddy bear?

   She paid $_____ for the teddy bear.

10. Justin has $29.
    He has $3 less than Tom.
    How much money does Tom have?

    Tom has $_____.

11. Write Yes or No.

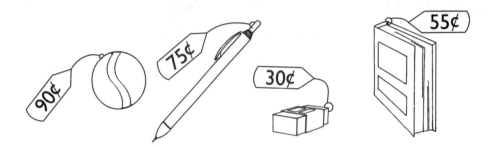

Susie has 70¢.

(a) Does she have enough money to buy the pen?

_____

(b) Does she have enough money to buy the eraser?

_____

(c) Does she have enough money to buy the notebook?

_____

(d) How much more does she need to buy the ball?

90 − 70 = _____

She needs _____¢ more to buy the ball.

12. Peter has 3 nickels.
John has 2 dimes.
David has 1 quarter.
Who has the most money?

_____ has the most money.

13. Adam paid 3 quarters and 1 nickel for a candy bar.
How much did the candy bar cost?

The candy bar cost _____ cents.

14.

(a) Jamal wants to buy the toy truck and the robot. How much money does he need?

$5 + $3 = $_____

He needs $_____.

(b) How much cheaper is the toy truck than the robot?

$5 − $3 = $_____

The toy truck is $_____ cheaper than the robot.

BLANK

BLANK